· HERDSMANSHIP ·

· HERDSMANSHIP ·

A guide for the herd owner, herdsman and cowman, on the
establishment and management of a pedigree herd of dairy cattle
of any breed, including the selection, breeding, feeding,
preparation for show and sale, how to judge, and on-the-farm
prevention and treatment of cattle diseases

Newman Turner

With a new foreword by Jerry Brunetti

Acres U.S.A.
Austin, TX

Herdsmanship

Acres U.S.A.
P.O. Box 91299
Austin, Texas 78709 U.S.A.
(512) 892-4400 • fax (512) 892-4448
info@acresusa.com • www.acresusa.com

Printed in the United States of America

Publisher's Cataloging-in-Publication

Turner, Newman, 1913-1964
Herdsmanship / Newman Turner. Austin, TX, ACRES U.S.A., 2009
    Reprint. Originally published: London: Faber and Faber Limited, 1952.
    xxx, 242 pp., 23 cm.
    Includes Index
    Includes Bibliography
    Incudes Illustrations
    ISBN 978-1-60173-010-7 (trade)

1. Organic farming. 2. Alternative agriculture. 3. Sustainable agriculture. 4. Agricultural ecology. 5. Organic fertilizers. I. Turner, Newman, 1913-1964 II. Title.

SF239.T9 2009   636.2

A Note from the Publisher . . .

It is with particular pride that we make the classic writings of Newman Turner on grass farming and natural health for cattle available to a new generation of organic farmers and graziers. A particularly sad note in our modern era of instantaneous digital information retrieval is the tendency to ignore older works. University librarians shake their heads in dismay as they note that students and researchers tend to delve into digital archives — many dating no further back than the 1990s — and scoff at any suggestion of entering the library stacks and dusting off vintage books.

Priceless insight can be found in the herd research of Randleigh Farm, the soils research of Professor William Albrecht, the traditional farming systems observations of F.H. King, or the pioneering writings of Sir Albert Howard, Lady Eve Balfour, André Voisin, Friend Sykes, Louis Bromfield, J.I. Rodale and others. Students of these great farmer-scientists, and others, quickly discern a level of sophistication still unparalleled by our modern-era reductionist scientists.

Most of the writings of these organic method pioneers were born during the beginning of the chemical era of agriculture. There was a fork in the road then, either toward sophisticated, diversified natural farming systems or chemical-based factory-style agriculture. History has recorded the fallout of the poor choice made back then in the statistics of depleted soils, poor crop quality, epidemic cancer and degenerative disease, and crippled farm economies.

Increasingly farmers and consumers are returning to healthier forms of food and farming. And the visionaries who stood firm at that earlier fork in the road still stand waiting to point the way to a new future.

In republishing Turner's writings, we've fought the temptation to modernize, Americanize, or heavily update these classic works. Obviously, currencies and their values change over a half-century. There are a few inputs and technologies that subsequent study have deemed inappropriate. And North American readers will have to pick up a few words of vocabulary as they translate from British English to American English. We present these books as they were published in the 1950s with only the slightest of annotation. A discerning reader who takes these books for what they are will walk away with a new understanding of the power and sophistication of the organic method and the beauty of farming in harmony with nature. And that reader will find lasting inspiration in Turner's love of land and beast and his plucky attitude toward the conventional wisdom of his day.

A special word of thanks must go to the sons of Newman Turner — Adam Newman Turner, Giles Newman Turner and Roger Newman Turner — for their trust in our stewardship of their father's written legacy and assistance in bringing these works back into reach of readers everywhere. The late American organic pioneer Bargyla Rateaver published editions of some of these works in the 1970s, which, like the originals, are now out of print. Like Newman Turner, she was clearly ahead of her time.

E.M. Forster wrote, "I suggest that the only books that influence us are those for which we are ready, and which have gone a little further down our particular path than we have yet got ourselves." Perhaps it is fitting that Newman Turner's farming and pasturing methods and insights into herd health are unveiled again today — after hiding in plain sight for these past decades — as interest in his brand of farming is at groundswell level. Untold numbers of new grass farmers will benefit from standing on this great's shoulders and learning anew from this simple farmer-scientist who has "gone a little further down our particular path than we have yet got ourselves."

Read, enjoy, and learn from the experiences and wisdom of fellow grass farmer Newman Turner.

October 2008

FRED C. WALTERS
AUSTIN, TEXAS

FOREWORD

Having read Newman Turner's *Fertility Farming* and *Fertility Pastures* some years ago, I was acquainted with Turner's sardonic wit, his unapologetic criticisms of what was then the beginnings of reductionistic agriculture and medicine, and his *persona non grata* in the newly emerging industrial farming clique. By today's organic standards, Turner would be considered an unadulterated purist; by today's conventional farming standards a fanatical, backward environmental zealot.

Turner wrote *Herdsmanship* twelve years after starting Goosegreen Farm in 1940, when England's darkest days appeared with the onset of World War II and when the agrarian ethic of being at peace not only with one another was prevalent, but when most smallholders were a lot more at peace with the natural world than what was to shortly follow. In 1952, England came out of a half decade of destruction of unprecedented proportions. On the wings of military victory came the nostrums and antidotes of that convulsion: miraculous antibiotics, pesticides derived from war chemicals, and nitrogen fertilizers derived from explosives manufacturing.

And with regard to animal epizootics, Turner decried the "final solution" — a militaristic remedy called depopulation — a "policy of utter despair" pointing out that wholesale slaughter of foot-and-mouth disease cattle achieved no effect in arresting the illness. In an editorial letter written to *Everybody's Weekly* decrying such a practice he rhetorically asks, "Should we slaughter the Minister of Agriculture and his staff when they get influenza, which is the equivalent in humans of foot and mouth disease?" In a chapter solely dedicated to foot and mouth disease, he details the remarkable evidence amassed by British researcher Sir Albert Howard who wrote in his book *Farming and Gardening for Health or Disease* that for 26 years in three provinces in India none of his healthy cattle contracted this highly contagious disease, in spite of them coming in direct contact with animals afflicted with it.

Turner implored the British government to conduct similar trials in order to prove that "there's only one disease of animals," which he proclaims "is not a devil that can be exorcised by magic potions or prevented by slaughter. It is the inevitable outcome of man's perversion of natural law."

Turner's chapters on maintaining livestock health and therapeutically reconciling existing ailments are surprisingly and probably, for many of us, disturbingly simplistic. Essentially, he emphasized that livestock illness is a result of bad farming practices and that good livestock health begins with true natural farming disciplines such as composting, bio-diverse pastures with deep-rooted forages and herbs, and sub-soiling, while also avoiding promoted panaceas that ignore or marginalize these fundamentals such as vaccines, pesticides, antibiotics and artificial fertilizers. He condemned the manufacturers of these products as having a vested interest in producing an "endless procession of remedies to chase the lengthening lines of new diseases." In short, he challenges the agricultural and veterinary industries to prove him wrong. "The fact is my treatments work, which is all that interests the farmer and livestock breeder." He makes a reverent reference to Pasteur's contemporary adversary, Bechamp, who of course denounced Pasteur's germ theory and proclaimed that the "terrain" was everything. Turner's answer to a cynical veterinarian praising the notability of Pasteur was, "I was not aware that Pasteur proved anything except there is a lot of money to be made by chemical and drug manufactures out of the almost criminal, and certainly blasphemous, theory that nature provided bacteria as a curse and not a blessing to human and animal kind".

Turner's remedies for cattle were those of nursing his stock back to health, as one would find in a health sanitarium for people in those days: fasting, cleansing (e.g. enemas), fresh air, sunlight, very few herbs, wild garlic (*Allium ursinum*) being the most relied on ("it is as near a cure-all as we are ever likely to get"). He respectfully acknowledges the work of herbalist and stockwoman Juliette de Bairacli Levy in her publication of *Herbal Handbook for Farm and Stable*. His approach to restoring animal health reminded me of the human "nature-cure" modalities of Jethro Kloss in *Back to Eden* published in 1939.

Today, over a half a century later, we have to deal with Turner's lamentations and frustrations as never before: mad cow disease, a growing epidemic of Johne's, and the resurgence of tuberculosis, bangs and foot and mouth. In addition, we have serious, unprecedented food poisoning outbreaks originating in animal fecal-soup cities, poisoning us with salmonella, *E. coli*, listeria and camphylobacter, annually hospitalizing millions and killing thousands. Yet Pasteur's ghost walks the halls of bureaucratic minions who steadfastly insist that depopulation is the foremost remedy on a family farm and that irradiating our foods is necessary to eradicate the filth originating in factory livestock facilities and on the walls of mega-abattoirs splattered with manure. They categorically identify and define viable family farming operations no differently than livestock concentration camps, thereby insisting that mandatory animal identification, via computer chips inserted into animals (NAIS), will somehow protect us from these inevitable, contagious and non-discriminating germs that they deem to be a national security issue. Turner would emphasize they are the messengers, not the cause of our agricultural system gone mad. He would challenge by example that these scourges which contemporary medicrats and technocrats wish to remediate by depopulation and the drenching of pesticides and antibiotics throughout all our ecosystems is the least effective and the most costly, regardless of how one defines "cost."

What Turner had going for him was that he had farming "credentials." That is, he was an award-winning pedigree Jersey breeder receiving numerous prizes and championships both for production and showing. His Jersey herd was the second best against all breeds in the National Competition, taking into consideration milk yield, butterfat, type, bulls, young stock and general management. His admiration and bias for the Jersey breed was without comparison or apology, yet he generously invites written contributions of eight well-known breeders, based upon their firsthand experiences with the Shorthorn, Guernsey, Kerry, Friesian, Dexter, Red Poll, Ayrshire and South Devon, including milk yields, temperament, body confirmation, points of the bull and so on, encouraging his reader to discern what breed best suits his own farm.

He writes an excellent chapter on herd profitability, including improving herd efficiency. Again, he emphasized that the cornerstones of profitability are rooted in herd health which in turn is rooted in the following: soil fertility and animal nutrition, cattle breeding for better feed efficiency and cattle breeding for longevity. I was quite heartened to read of his belief that breeding for longevity was "the most important factor of all . . . and that good old (cows) are a better breeding bet than good young ones." Again, Turner emphasizes that longevity is not only a matter of animal genetics but ". . . often a result of fertility farming methods . . ." Longevity would reduce costs of production and disease and death would be reduced to a minimum.

Newman's chapter on economics detailing the analysis of costs of production, yields, net cost per gallon of milk, cost per cow, returns in labor, cow capital, feed costs, depreciation, etc. is as useful as any primer in practical agricultural economics. Being the pedigree breeder that he was, he could provide the most useful and affordable approaches to building a profitable show herd with the breeding stock that provides the cashflow and pride associated with such an enterprise, all while taking judicious care of the farm, its soil, pastures, hedgerows and beautiful livestock by happy engaged families who reverently steward their land.

It's a pity that the animal science majors — as I was one — attending colleges and universities during the '50s, '60s and '70s weren't privy to the land- and people-friendly practices exemplified by Turner that were extraordinary examples of natural farming success. Turner, in my opinion, was one the century's ecological and scientific farming giants. Along with his peers like Louis Bromfield, William Kenan of Randleigh Farms, Sir Albert Howard and Prof. William Albrecht, Turner deserves the recognition and commemoration in a Natural Farming Hall of Fame.

October 2007   JERRY BRUNETTI
                                          MARTINS CREEK, PENNSYLVANIA

> *Jerry Brunetti is an internationally recognized consultant*
> *on natural animal care and a formulator of nutraceutical*
> *products for livestock, particularly dairy cows.*

Reading Newman Turner . . .

Modern-day readers might have to adjust their vocabulary as they read this historic work, particularly those readers in North America. Following are a few thoughts on some specific terms Turner uses:

Catarrh – read as *inflammation of a mucous membrane.*

Corn – read as *grains.*

Dredge corn – read as *mixed cereals and legumes.*

Herbal ley – Today this would be called a rotational grazing cell, a paddock, or pasture. He emphasized a mix of grasses, clover and herbs. Turner made use of standard grasses such as timothy, meadow fescue, orchard grass and perennial ryegrass. Into this he added the herbs chicory, yarrow, plantain, burnet and sheep's parsley as they are deep rooted and concentrate a wide range of minerals, more so than the grasses.

Ley – read as *temporary pasture,* or a rotational cell or paddock.

Lucerne – read as *alfalfa.*

Maize – read as *corn.*

Manuring – read as *fertilizing.* What would be called *manure spreading* in North America would be described by Turner as *manuring with FYM (farmyard manure).*

Project – read as *program.*

Pulses – read as *legumes.*

About the Author

Frank Newman Turner was one of the founders of the modern environmental movement and published some of the first organic farming and gardening magazines. He founded *The Farmer,* the first organic quarterly magazine "published and edited from the farm," became a founding council member of the Soil Association, the U.K.'s leading regulator of organic standards, and served as president of an early organic horticultural organization. As a farmer, he received numerous awards in animal breeding and horticulture. A true visionary, many of his agricultural innovations are only now being rediscovered by the new wave of organic farmers and graziers.

He was born in September 1913, the eldest son of tenant farmers near Barnsley, Yorkshire, England. After graduating in agriculture and dairying at Leeds University, he became an inspector with the Potato Marketing Board. His journalistic skills soon became apparent, and he wrote regular columns for the British publications *Farmers Weekly* and *Farmer and Stockbreeder.* He met his future wife Lorna while he was on a business trip to Cornwall, and they married in 1939.

An Independent Mind

The dedication in F. Newman Turner's first book, *Fertility Farming,* is, "To my mother, who taught me to think for myself." This quality came to the fore as World War II approached, and he registered as a conscientious objector. He had become a Quaker and attended lectures by Dick Sheppard and other prominent pacifists of the time. Humanitarian principles were to guide him for the rest of his life. In 1940, he and Lorna, with their newborn son, moved to the edge of the Chilton Polden Hills in Somerset, England, where he was to manage Goosegreen, a mixed farm of about 200 acres, for conscientious objectors. Here he began experiments in organic husbandry inspired by the writings and personal encouragement of Sir Albert Howard, the author of the classics *An Agricultural Testament* and *Farming and Gardening for Health or Disease.*

When the war ended Turner bought Goosegreen and continued his experiments in creating "health from the soil up." The plow soon became redundant. He believed that fertility lay in the subsoil and was best sustained by minimal disturbance. Deep-rooting herbal leys, or planting blends for pasture, formed the basis of healthy stock — in Turner's case a herd of prize-winning pedigree Jerseys. Ailments among the cattle and draft horses — and children — were treated by fasting, enemas and dosing with herbal infusions.

F. Newman Turner launched the magazine *The Farmer* in 1946. It soon gained a devoted, if small, following in many parts of the world. He also set up the Institute of Organic Husbandry, which presented a series of weekend courses at Goosegreen. Practical instruction was given in composting, pruning, tripoding, and silage-making while Lorna served tea with homebaked scones made from stone-ground flour. A Whole Food Society was established in 1946 to put producers in touch with consumers who wanted organic produce.

Richard de la Mare of the London publishing firm Faber and Faber, who was among many visitors to Goosegreen, persuaded Turner to write the trilogy of organic farming books published in the early '50s, *Fertility Farming, Fertility Pastures,* and *Herdsmanship.* He added the booklet *Cure Your Own Cattle* to his literary output.

At about this time, Lawrence D. Hills started writing for *The Farmer.* His great mission was to establish comfrey as a major contribution to the postwar effort to feed the world. Using the Bocking strain that he had developed, he established the Great Comfrey Race in 1954. Russian Comfrey, introduced to the U.K. in the 1870s by Henry Doubleday, a Quaker smallholder, was believed to be a valuable source of protein and animal fodder. A number of farmers and horticulturalists competed for the record yields, and Lawrence D. Hills reported on their progress in the magazine *The Farmer.*

Again, F. Newman Turner led the field, growing 23 tons of comfrey per acre at Ferne Farm, Shaftesbury, Dorset, to which the family had moved in 1953. In 1958 Lawrence Hills founded the Henry Doubleday Research Association, now named Garden Organic, and invited Turner to serve as its first president.

Natural Health for Man & Beast

Many cattlemen knew of Turner's considerable experience with the natural treatment of animals . . . and he often treated their ailing cows successfully when conventional treatments had failed. Owners asked, "My cow did so well; can you suggest anything for a problem of my own?" So Turner decided to qualify as a medical herbalist and naturopath. The farming phase of his career came to an end, and the family moved to Letchworth Garden City in Hertfordshire, about an hour outside London. Although *The Farmer* closed down, Turner continued to publish its subsection, *The Gardener,* as a monthly magazine. It was probably the first exclusively organic gardening periodical. He also edited and published *Fitness and Health from Herbs,* the magazine of the U.K.'s National Institute of Medical Herbalists.

Although he was a committed pacifist, Frank Newman Turner showed no reticence in communicating his belief that both animal and human health demanded respect for and cooperation with nature. Such ideals were at loggerheads with the powerful agrochemical and pharmaceutical industries, and Turner was no stranger to controversy. In the early 1950s, at the height of the Foot and Mouth Disease epidemic, he challenged the Ministry of Agriculture to allow him to take infected animals into his herd to prove the immunity of naturally reared stock. They refused, of course, preferring to pursue the expensive slaughter policies which still continue in the Foot and Mouth and BSE crises of our day.

His innate pugnacity, the stresses inherent in his various enterprises, not least the problems of publishing on a shoestring, and what turned out to be a genetic predisposition to heart disease, proved a lethal combination. In June 1964, while visiting herbal medicine suppliers in Germany, Turner died suddenly of a coronary thrombosis. He was 50 years old. Frank Newman Turner was one of a small band of visionaries who laid the foundations for the modern environmental revolution. He always maintained that health began in the soil, and this message continues to be carried most effectively from the grassroots — the small-scale farmers and horticulturalists who uphold organic principles. The increasing awareness of mankind's duty to nature would have delighted him.

ROGER NEWMAN TURNER, B.Ac., N.D., D.O.
Letchworth Garden City, England

Roger Newman Turner, the eldest of F. Newman Turner's three sons, is a practicing naturopath, osteopath and acupuncturist. He speaks and writes on complementary and alternative therapies for human health.

HERDSMANSHIP

by

NEWMAN TURNER

A guide for the herd owner, herdsman and cowman, on the establishment and management of a pedigree herd of dairy cattle of any breed, including the selection, breeding, feeding, preparation for show and sale, how to judge, and on-the-farm prevention and treatment of cattle diseases.

Acres U.S.A.

Austin, TX

Praise for *Herdsmanship*

"In this record of successful cattle farming the reader will find guidance on the establishment of a herd, preparation for the cattle show, management for milk production, and the prevention and treatment of disease."

— The Times Literary Supplement

"Delightfully written and well illustrated, this book provides much food for thought. . . . It is a book which makes pleasant and interesting reading and certainly should be added to the farm bookshelf."

— The Home Farmer

" . . . will undoubtedly receive a warm welcome from a new generation of scientifically-minded modern herdsmen, well-versed in the up-to-date theories as well as the ancient skills of their art. Written by a farmer who at the age of twelve was regularly milking a dozen cows daily and who has since taken numerous prizes and championships in both inspection and production classes in many big shows. It bears the mark of authenticity."

— Field

TO

THE JERSEY COW
WHICH COMBINES BEAUTY
WITH EFFICIENCY

CONTENTS

Section One

ESTABLISHING THE HERD AND THE BASIS OF PRACTICAL BREEDING

Section Two

THE SHOWING AND JUDGING OF DAIRY CATTLE

Section Three

MANAGEMENT FOR MILK PRODUCTION

Section Four

CATTLE DISEASES—PREVENTION TREATMENT

APPENDICES

LIST OF ILLUSTRATIONS

PREFACE

W hile this book seeks to be comprehensive in the subject of dairy cow selection and management, it is nevertheless confined to information and guidance which as a whole is not available in any other book that I know. But I have assumed certain elementary knowledge, such for instance as the fact that a cow is milked by squeezing the teats or applying suction by means of an alternating mechanically made vacuum, and the need to give a cow a couple of months' rest between each lactation. The basic elements of dairy farming are available from a thousand sources. The desire which has inspired *this* book is to impart from my *own* experiences the knowledge and the enthusiasm which makes cowmen and cow-keepers into herdsmen and pedigree cattle breeders. Above all I want to show how it is possible so to simplify and modify the work of dairy farming as to make it a truly scientific and mutually happy association between cattle and men.

The immense and increasing toll of disease in our dairy herds need never be, and the young and rising generation of herdsmen and herd-owners who are at last beginning to adopt the commonsense methods introduced in my book, *Fertility Farming* and supplemented in this book, know that in *their* herds at any rate, it will not be.

As the son of a working tenant farmer in Yorkshire, I milked my first cow at the age of five, I regularly milked a dozen cows morning and night when I was twelve and I have been milking cows ever since. From being my father's cowman, through periods of assisting other herdowners I became my own herdsman when I took on Goosegreen Farm twelve years ago. I have been my own herdsman ever since. But I haven't always had to milk all my own cows. For first my wife and later my good Italian friend, Toni Capozzoli, milked the cows along with me morning and night, until Toni eventually took charge of the milking himself. Together we have developed a herd which has won numerous prizes and championships, both for production and inspection at all the main shows in the south-west, and as I complete this book I am informed that in the Somerset County Herds Competitions (which take account of milk yields, butter-fat, type, bulls, young stock and general management), we had the second best Jersey herd; second only to the herd which was supreme against all breeds in the National Competition. Though I continue to be my own herdsman to this day, I could not have written this book without the devoted cowmanship of my wife in the early years and Toni for the past eight years, or the tireless attention to the manuscript of my secretary, Rae Thompson. My deepest gratitude is theirs for making my part in the joint effort possible.

March 1952   F. NEWMAN TURNER

ACKNOWLEDGEMENTS

I am grateful to the Editor of *The Farmers' Weekly* for permission to use some material which I first wrote for his journal and to the following secretaries of cattle breed societies for the judging points of their breeds used in the Appendix on the 'Why and How of the Breeds'; Mr. Edward Ashby of the English Jersey Cattle Society; Mr. M. F. J. Batting of the Dexter Cattle Society; Mr. W. H. Bursby of the British Friesian Cattle Society; Mr. S. H. Dingley of the Ayrshire Cattle Society; Mr. A. Furneaux, Secretary of the Coates Herd Book (Shorthorns); Mr. R.O. Hubl of the Kerry Cattle Society; Mr. R. F. Johnson formerly of the South Devon Cattle Society (who is now Secretary of the National Pig Breeders' Association); Col. T. M. Kerr of the English Guernsey Cattle Society; Mr. A. C. Burton of the Red Poll Cattle Society. The breeders themselves who have described their methods and their breeds have my warmest gratitude.

I am specially grateful to Brian Branston for permission to quote lengthy extracts from his book, *Breeding for Production*, Lawrence D. Hills, who read my manuscript and made valuable suggestions, and Douglas Allen for many of the photographs.

My thanks are also due to the Principals of Wye College, the Royal Agricultural College, Cirencester, and Mr. F. J. Rigby for the comparative costings on page 27.

I would also like to offer my thanks for photographs of plates 1 and 2 to West Midland Photo Services Ltd., Shrewsbury; plate 3, *Wiltshire Gazette*; plate 5, Independent Newspapers Ltd., Dublin; plate 28, G. S. McCann, Uttoxeter; plate 33, English Jersey Cattle Society; plates 34, 38 and 47, *Farmer & Stockbreeder*; plate 35, Mr. G. F. Dee Shapland; plate 37, R. Hobbs; plates 39,42 and 48, Sport & General Press Agency, London; plates 43 and 44, Lady Loder; plates 45 and 46, A. E. K. Cull; plate 50, Nicholas Home Ltd., Totnes. All other photographs are by Douglas Allen of Bridgwater.

Section One

ESTABLISHING THE HERD
AND
THE BASIS OF PRACTICAL
BREEDING

Chapter 1

MY START IN HERDSMANSHIP

There are cows and cows, and the animals with which I started my lessons in herdsmanship on my father's farm in Yorkshire were just cows. Any question of a breed never occurred to us. But we valued our animals and studied their needs even more than the few hobby farmers who at that time owned pedigree herds. Even as recently as that time, thirty-odd years ago, we were completely oblivious of the many diseases which beset the animal breeder of today; veterinary surgeons devoted most of their time to horses; the maintenance of health in the herd was mainly a matter of growing good food and feeding it to the cows in adequate quantity. The successful farmer was the man with an instinct about animals; a knowledge of viruses and bacteria was not necessary. Farming was an art and not an industry beggared with 'scientists' and petty officials. Farming could only properly be performed by men who had it in their bones; there was little hope for the man who had put it all in his head. There was no ready-made answer available in a book, and very few ready-made remedies served up by the manufacturing chemists, though even then they were already founding their fortunes on the farmer's misfortunes.

Though our cows were no particular breed at all, for want of a name they were generally considered to be Shorthorns. That must be no reflection on the Shorthorn breed of to-day. It is merely the fact that the Shorthorn breed embraces such a wide variety of colours that for general purposes an unidentifiable cow was called a Shorthorn, just as today a black-and-white cow, whatever its origin, is considered by the commercial farmer to be a Friesian, though pedigree breeders deplore this loose use of breed description. Strictly speaking, I suppose the words cross-bred should precede the use of a breed name where a pedigree is not available, or even when the animal is not registered in the official herd book. But the difference between a registered and an unregistered animal meant little to us. Breeds for us were distinguishable by colour rather than names in a book in London.

What characterized our cows was the uncertainty with which they transmitted their propensities to their offspring, if at all. This provided us with a certain thrill of anticipation each time a cow was to give birth. But the bank manager rarely found that thrill a satisfactory substitute for the economical yields which planned breeding would have produced. Consequently as often as a good cow gave us a heifer as good as herself or better, she gave us a dud which was quite incapable of a profitable life in the herd. This complicated our farming by making it necessary for us to dabble in beef production, mixing it as need arose with milk production, and because of the difficulty of properly assessing the potentialities of each heifer until she had done a lactation, it meant we were engaged in the least profitable kind of beef production, that is cow beef or at best, heifer beef, whenever our guesses about the milk production capability of the animals we bred failed to come off.

Similarly when I started farming on my own account at Goose-green, I took on a good commercial herd of Shorthorns which had a slight sprinkling of Friesians and their crosses. Though in our first year or two we were able, by heavy feeding, to get the herd average up to about 700 gallons, which was extremely good as a start with non-pedigree cattle, their daughters didn't even approach that yield, excepting the occasional fluke, though we used three different pedigree Shorthorn bulls. Yet the daughters of the only *pedigree* cow we had, a Friesian, by different Shorthorn bulls, all did slightly better than she (though she herself was a 1,200-gallon cow). It became clear to me then that I must have cattle which, like my Friesian, had behind them some ancestry of transmission certainty. And this could only be got by pedigree breeding. Pedigree breeding has often been called a rich man's hobby, but this experience demonstrated that in my case at any rate it was likely to be a poor man's passport to profits. And indeed it proved to be. I decided to change over to exclusively pedigree cattle, and it was as though I had been blindfold until that time, for breeding for milk production became a simple process of planning, whereas before it had been impossible guesswork.

There were other factors which helped my decision to change over to pedigree cattle, the chief of which was disease in the herd which made some drastic changes necessary and provided an opportunity to bring in a pedigree nucleus. But I will say more about that in a later chapter, as in another chapter, too, I will explain my choice of breed. But the fact of disease, especially abortion and tuberculosis, decided me to

4

change over gradually, replacing the Shorthorns as they calved down, with pedigree Jerseys.

There are two systems of founding a dairy herd, both of which are reasonably safe for the inexperienced buyer. One is to go to an established herd, which has shown consistent breeding over a number of years and buy a nucleus of heifers with good production figures immediately behind them, and a bull of the same family. The other is to buy old cows that have done good records, in-calf if possible so that you have at least a calf to come if the cow herself is at the end of her career. The old cows should, if possible, be of the same strain so that you start one step along the path of your breeding policy, but don't be too rigid about the strain if the cow you want is good. It is useless to buy a cow because she is of the strain you want if she happens to be a particularly poor specimen of that strain, though it is not impossible to buy a good fluke in that way. I once did. But once in a lifetime is as much as you can expect.

My 'fluke' was bought at a Jersey Show and Sale at Reading. She had won nothing in the ring, her highest lactation yield had been 400 gallons, she had a badly shaped udder, but she was a pleasant-looking animal and of extremely good breeding. She first came into the sale ring and was bought for 100 guineas by a very famous breeder. Why, it is difficult to imagine, for she would not have made any contribution to his already fabulous herd. Perhaps he was buying for a beginner, friend, or neighbour. But he changed his mind and the cow came back into the ring at the end of the sale with the explanation that she had been bought by mistake and was being offered again by her purchaser. This, of course, aroused suspicion. But being compelled by some inner impulse, a hunch, if you like, though I think hunches generally have a little evidence to support them, when the bids got to 40 guineas and stuck, I decided that at such a price she was worth buying as a foster mother for some calves I had. I got her for 60 guineas. She never did anything more than 400 gallons—her udder just wasn't made for more—but she bred me three good daughters, one of which gave 1,000 gallons with her first calf, and 1,500 with her second at 5.6 percent butterfat, the second I sold before I knew the capabilities of her sister, and the third looks like doing as well as the first.

But that is just one of those things that never happens again. It is as well in laying the foundations of a herd to forget that such possibilities exist, and don't be tempted by what appears to be cheap unless there are factors affecting the price which you know about and can remedy, but about which competing buyers are ignorant.

Chapter 2

SELECTING AND FOUNDING THE HERD

In spite of the gamble involved in buying at sales I felt my capital was not enough to enable me to do much buying privately from breeders. I thought I knew enough about cattle to avoid the worst troubles. Yet there was hardly an animal of the foundation cattle of my Jersey herd which did not have some trouble, and of about fifty females I bought in the first five years, only three of them stayed five years and what is more they stayed only as a result of my own success with the natural treatment of disease. One of them was sterile, another a habitual milk fever case, and the third had mastitis in two quarters when I got her home from a sale. All the others, bought both privately and at sales, have left this life because they suffered from some defect of health.

I do strongly advise newcomers to pedigree breeding to place themselves in the hands of a reputable breeder and take what heifers he can offer at a reasonable price, or let him find someone else's worth buying and pay him for doing it. It will be money well spent if you can persuade an experienced man to do it. I fear, however, most breeders would consider it too much of a responsibility.

When I wanted to buy a bunch of heifers in Jersey I had no knowledge of conditions there and employed a breeder to conduct me from farm to farm and seek out suitable animals for sale at the price I was prepared to pay. At the end of a day touring the island and buying ten heifers I paid him £35 commission. At the time I was most reluctant to do so. But the animals did survive which is more than could be said for those I bought myself in England.

In England I didn't think myself in need of expert advice, and in consequence I paid very much more the other way by buying animals entirely on my own responsibility and taking the very costly consequences.

I followed both systems referred to in establishing my herd. I bought privately seven bulling heifers, and their half-brother. They were run with their half-brother with the idea of starting a breeding policy a step ahead of myself, so to speak. It didn't come off, for each one of these heifers produced either a dead calf, or a bull, and all but one died before they produced me a single live heifer calf. Of my original nucleus of heifers I have no descendant for most of them had had husk when I bought them, though it was not evident at the time. They nearly all got into a serious condition with parasitic pneumonia and became useless before calving their second calves. One died of acetonaemia (my first case and the only one I've failed with). One only survived. So much for my efforts to establish a line bred herd. But I still believe the best method of starting is the purchase of heifers from a reliable breeder with, if necessary, the assistance of another experienced breeder.

The other way—buying old cows—brought me almost as much trouble but it *did* produce some calves and it was really from this miscellaneous collection of old cows that I built my present herd. This is a slower way of establishing a herd, for unless the cows are all of similar strains, the concentrating of characteristics cannot be controlled except through the bull. This means that the first crop of heifers carry only a half of the particular breeding that is wanted, whereas in the case of heifers of the same strain as the bull the resulting heifers carry a double concentration of the breeding. And if both the bull and the heifers are themselves line bred from consistently healthy long-lived and good-producing animals then profitable and consistent breeding is almost certain to continue. But few of us can expect our herd building to start so well. Mine, by the failure of the vital nucleus of heifers which I got to mate with the bull, certainly didn't, so I got off to a one-legged start; it did nevertheless enable me to introduce a slightly different strain to improve the one I had originally chosen, and by this blend of breeding develop my own strain of strong-bodied efficient converters of home-grown food, which I could not have found ready-made for me in any of the recognized strains, and certainly not in the fashionable strains.

The question of whether or not to pay high prices is one which must trouble those with the money available. For the man with limited capital the problem is whether to buy a few at the top prices, or more at lower prices. For both types of buyers, it is wise to get the best that money can buy and few rather than many. A few good cows, done well, will pay better than a lot of second-rate animals done moderately well. The animals which make record prices at auction sales may be left well alone, for the price is probably being paid for some fashion fad or some freak performance. The payers of record prices are generally wealthy industrial magnates and not sound judges of a good cow, though they often employ men who *are* sound judges. An alternative policy, if financially possible, is to buy young animals (stirks, perhaps) and only a very few milkers. That means waiting two years or more before the herd *begins* to become a milk-producing unit: and of course it requires capital. But decide upon the cows you really want, with the help of an experienced breeder if necessary, and be prepared to pay well. The few comparatively high-priced animals will multiply more quickly than you would imagine and patience in accepting a rather lower milk cheque for the sake of really sound animals will be well repaid in the quality and value of the resultant home-bred heifers.

If you must have a good-sized milk cheque coming in, then hang on to some of your best yielding commercial cows (if you are changing over from a commercial to a pedigree herd), or if you are starting from scratch, buy a few heavy yielding old cows which have two or three lactations to come. Whether or not these old cows are of the chosen breed, or commercial cross-bred animals, will depend on the price at which they can be found, and whether or not you have the patience to tolerate a mixed herd for a number of years.

Having a Shorthorn and Friesian cross-bred herd and being very limited for capital when I decided to change over to pedigree Jerseys I had not much choice in the matter. I bought my bunch of seven heifers and their half-brother for the nucleus of my future herd and then, in order to keep the income going I brought in old Jersey cows as I sold out the cross-breds. But I made the mistake in the beginning of buying freshly calved old cows in order to get milk quickly and many of them had obviously been sold as difficult or declining breeders. For in some cases they never bred again. There can be no means of protecting the buyer against breeders who sell animals which have finished breeding, but it is hard on a young farmer, just starting with very limited capital, to have to pay an established and successful breeder 100 guineas, as I did on one occasion in the early years, when 100 guineas was not a modest price to anyone and was a small fortune to me, and to have no redress. It is part of the game at the moment. But the time *must* come when sales under the auspices of the breed societies are confined to cattle guaranteed in udder, breeding and milk yield. Anything which cannot be so guaranteed must go into the commercial market and be bought by the man who has the money to squander or the courage to take a chance. But I have more to say on the need of cattle sales reforms later (see page 32. Chapter 5.)

If, instead of freshly calved animals, in-calvers are bought, at least one has the chance of getting a heifer calf should the cow herself prove to be a bad breeder. But the risk with in-calvers is that they are being sold for udder trouble, which will fire up when the udder freshens for calving. It is therefore doubly necessary in buying dry in-calf cows to examine the udder with extreme care. Experience of my mastitis treatment (page 121) will give confidence to buy animals in spite of threatened mastitis for if the cow is treated immediately she calves there is no reason why she shouldn't be cured. But for buyers who as yet have no experience of my treatments, more caution is necessary. Defects to guard against are hardening or thickening of the teat channel or pea-like lumps or obstructions in the teat channel. When the liquid is drawn from the teats it should be a sticky, gummy 'honey' which, though clear with a heifer in calf for the first time, will be slightly cloudy with a cow that has had a calf. Avoid the watery or highly coloured discharge. Be confident with the clearer honey-like discharge which indicates a dry udder in perfect health which will not go down with any kind of trouble at calving time.

Other important guides to the health and productive ability of a cow may be mentioned here as a help to prospective buyers, for little enough protection is given to the buyer and while breed societies are governed by vendors I see no great prospect of improvement. These points do not strictly come under the eye of the judge in the show ring, so I mention them now, instead of in my chapter on judging.

The *vulva* should be soft, pliable and a healthy pink colour when the folds are drawn apart. A tough leathery or hardened vulva with pale coloration is one of the signs of a difficult breeder, for it is the mirror of an unhealthy uterus within. Spots of catarrh or discoloured discharge from the vulva or on the walls of the vagina when opened for examination are an indication of leucorrhea or other uterine discharge which while it continues will prevent breeding.

Any discharge from a cow close to or just after calving should be clear and free from white flecks. Any discoloration or catarrhal appearance is a sure sign of a diseased uterus. This is not to say that it cannot be cured; it quite easily can be by my treatment for sterility (page 131), but allowance should be made for this in estimating the value of the cow.

Fat around the tail setting and pin bones is a sign of sluggish reproductive organs. A bony tail setting and pin bones with complete absence of surplus flesh or fat in those regions are the mark of a good breeder and hard-working cow.

Tail setting. A definite dip in front of the tail setting or farther forward or a very marked sagging of the loins may mean a mechanical interference with the proper functioning of the uterus and should be avoided.

The swollen or 'big' knee, though very occasionally due to a knock, is almost invariably caused by an accumulation of toxins in the system. The gathering of this accumulation around the knee joint is nature's protection for the reproductive organs and lungs of the cow. But it is an obvious sign that the cow is in a toxic condition and would benefit by an internal cleansing treatment such as I have set out for sterility (page 131). It is almost certain that, though at the outset a big knee is harmless, if the feeding and general management which gave rise to it are persistently continued, the ability of the system to localize the accumulation in places where it can do little or no harm will be lost, for there is a limit to the amount of rubbish the system can deal with. After the knees—the uterus or lungs must be used as channels of discharge; then real trouble follows.

Eyes should be bright and intelligent. If you can't get a clear and colourful reflection of yourself in the cow's eye she can't be in good health. A dull eye is the window of a sour stomach and a sad heart; pass it by!

Mouth. Teeth should be straight, evenly placed in the gum, and of course, all there. Jaws should meet evenly all round and be neither under nor overshot. Either of these faults will interfere with grazing, though the cow could live well on hay, silage and other stall feeding, and such an animal, if born into the herd, should not be destroyed. Indeed some calves may be born with undershot jaws which correct themselves as they grow older.

Skin must be thin, loose and pliable, especially over the ribs. A handful of skin pulled away from the ribs should come away easily, feel silky in the fingers, and go back like soft elastic when released.

Chapter 3

PRACTICAL BREEDING
AND SIMPLE GENETICS

Having selected the cows, successful breeding demands some knowledge of genetics; some farmers have an uncanny ability almost to know by looking at a cow and a bull whether they will milk well if mated. But such ability is only for the few whose animal instinct amounts to genius. Mr. George Odlum, the famous breeder of the Manningford Friesians, in his writings and lectures says much about transmission, recessive factors, genes and other involved genetical theory, but in spite of his immense and detailed knowledge I credit much of his breeding success to a mixture of genius and good luck.

Those of us who can expect neither of these are left with ample opportunity to acquire good judgement and wide experience. Both grow with use and in that respect we may score over the mere lucky genius.

But there is no need to wade through the many books on the subject of animal genetics in order to acquire the knowledge which makes a good livestock breeder, though it is well worth any breeder's or herdsman's while to get as much book knowledge as may be obtained from the excellent little book, *Breeding for Production*, by Brian Branston (Faber). This will cut out a few of the unknown factors in the practical breeding side—but the only real way of learning breeding is to breed. Put Bull A on cows B, C, and D, and see if the results are AB, AC, AD. Study the progeny beside their parents and see for yourself which characteristics have been inherited from which parents, and which appear to have come from nowhere. With an old breed like the Jersey it is a fairly safe gamble that A on B will produce AB, but with some breeds, especially dual-purpose breeds which carry both flesh and milk factors, not even an Odlum can forecast the result. Consistent breeding of dual-purpose cattle can without question be achieved, and some of our leading Red Poll and South Devon herds in particular are outstanding examples of consistent breeding, but the process is longer and the beginner may expect consistent results more quickly and more easily from the breeds which have concentrated on milk or butter yields, and have produced animals with only one, or at most production purposes.

Far more can be learned about breeding by looking at cows and bulls, their progeny and their records, than by looking at books. Many a townsman has scoffed at the farmer wasting his time 'leaning on the gate', but if his animals are in the field, that is how he learns and improves upon his skill as a livestock breeder; that is how he improves upon his crops. Farmers nowadays have all too little time to lean on the gate and think, which is a pity, for I am quite sure that moments of contemplation and moments observing the growing crop or the grazing animal are the farmer's most profitable moments, materially as well as spiritually.

I could tell you the sire of any of my home-bred females, merely by looking them hard in the face, and I have eight bulls in use. Admittedly this is not easy in the first days of a calf's life, but as the calf grows to maturity the characteristics of both parents become plainly evident to the observant. This kind of observance is the only way to know exactly whether the breeding policy is working out right or wrong.

Because I think Mr. Branston has provided in farmer's or herdsman's language the essential knowledge of genetics, I will quote some valuable extracts which I endorse. I hope these extracts give an outline of an excellent and absorbingly interesting book which will make every farmer, breeder or herdsman who reads this book, read also, for the full story of sensible breeding, Brian Branston's book. In any case they provide the 'heart' of the subject which will enable readers of my book to grasp the basic knowledge of animal genetics necessary for the practical man:

'Hereditary

'An animal which may breed one way or the other for a certain factor I shall call a *mixed-breeder* for that factor. (The geneticist calls such animals *heterozygotes*.)

'The practical breeder of animals for utility must always be on the look-out for animals which are mixed-breeders for the factors which help to make his living so that normally he can bar those animals from his breeding plans; just as he must search for and retain those animals which are *self-breeders* (homozygotes) for the factors he needs.... What is the breeder to do when the outward appearance of animals is similar but their breeding performance is different?

'An example to illustrate outward similarity and different genetical make-up can be taken from Mendel's sweet-pea experiments. Mendel found that some peas were self-breeders for red flowers and some for white flowers: when he crossed a red with a white he got *all* red offspring. But if he mated two of these first-generation reds together he got offspring in the proportion of *three* reds to *one* white.

'Obviously, in this coupling the first cross red offspring only *appear* to be like their red parent, because no matter how many self-breeding red parents you mate together you will always get red offspring: if you had only red marbles in a bag no matter how often you shook up the bag you would always pick out a red one. But in mating together red offspring of sweet peas where the one parent was self-breeding red and the other self-breeding white you get a proportion of three reds to one white. When a trait in one of the parents dominated another, as the red dominates the white in the red and white pea parents, Mendel called that trait *dominant*. The white he called *recessive* because although it had disappeared entirely in the first cross offspring, it nevertheless came out in the crosses between those offspring: it had only *receded* into the background.

'If we were to continue breeding from the second-generation flowers we should find that one red would be a self-breeder for red; two reds would be mixed-breeders for red and white in the proportion 3 : 1, and the white would be a self-breeder for white … one red breeds true, two reds breed untrue, and one white breeds true. In other words, the appearance of two of the reds is not what it seems. This comes home to the dairy farmer, say, when he realizes that some of his best yielders for both milk and butterfat may possess those qualities only as the first cross sweet peas possessed the colour red: they may be mixed-breeders for both factors. This is indeed tragic when one remembers that the average number of calves born to dairy cows in this country at present is only a little over two. *Both* of these may quite easily be the two mixed breeders out of the four. If, in addition, the farmer's bull should turn out to be a mixed-breeder for milk and butterfat then he could do great damage in the herd. It is unfortunate that it is impossible by looking at a cow or a bull to tell whether it is a mixed-breeder or a self-breeder for milk yield and high butterfat. We cannot tell this even by looking at its parents or grandparents; nor by studying its pedigree; nor, if it is a female, by studying its milk yields (that is only comparable to looking at the red first cross of the red and white sweet peas and seeing that it is red); nor, yet again, by studying the records of the milk yields of its dam.

'The only sure way of distinguishing a self-breeder from a mixed-breeder is by sampling their offspring: the inescapable conclusion is that you can only tell how an animal breeds by finding out how it has already bred. 'By their fruits ye shall know them.'

'Since a farmer needs as far as possible to keep animals which are self-breeding for the most perfect set of inherited qualities, and since a start has to be made somewhere, he must get together complete data about the breeding performance of his animals used for reproduction. There must be no hiding of defects. A farmer who tries to work without records is playing blindman's buff among his cattle. A pedigree breeder who hides defects in the stock he intends to sell is Agriculture's Fifth Columnist....'

'Inbreeding

'*Inbreeding is the one certain way to bring into being self-breeding groups of animals, to diminish variability, to give uniformity.*

'Inbreeding will always result automatically in self-breeding animals; but the important thing for the practical breeder to realize is that *those animals can be self-breeding for defects as well as for good qualities.* The farmer must decide and then select those animals which are to be inbred, his purpose always being to bring together the greatest number of good qualities and the least number of bad qualities which will be fixed in his self-breeding stock. Breeders should never start inbreeding with inferior stock, in fact they should never start inbreeding with a group of animals in which the best are not quite as good as their owners would wish them to be.

'Inbreeding coupled with selection is the quickest way to produce self-breeding animals—animals which will transmit as they express.

'Neither is selection the same thing as culling. Culling is the traditional method of raising the standard of a dairy herd or a laying flock of hens—and *it is wrong as a standard method* for a number of reasons. Culling (as in the case of recessive "reds") does nothing to *raise* the quality of the flock or herd; if the breeders remain untouched then another crop of culls must automatically come along. Economically, culling alone as a standard practice year after year is foolish. In a dairy herd, for instance, low yielders are culled *after* they have made their low yields (more often after *two or three* low yields than just one—because they have been given "another chance"). This means they are culled after the owner has lost money. The sort of herd a commercial dairy farmer will have fifteen years from to-day depends not on the cows he culls but on the sort of bulls he uses in the

14

meantime. It is bulls not culls that are important. In present conditions the commercial dairy farmer with a small herd of up to fifteen cows would be better off not culling but using his worst yielders to breed beef stores.

'The owner of a pedigree herd of milk cattle on the other hand needs to cull and cull hard to eliminate the low-yielding individual and even more so the low-yielding family. But he must cull with a knowledge of the genetical make-up of his animals—he must cull from a knowledge of the individual's power of transmission as well as its expression. When he does this he turns culling into selection. Culling is a negative practice and leaves the situation much as it was; selection is a positive thing and makes for improvement. . . .

'Part of the stigma which appears to be attached to inbreeding is not due to man's own conventions of morality, it is a result of economic loss from aberrant offspring which have cropped out where inbreeding has been tried.

'These aberrant offspring are *not caused* by inbreeding, they are caused by aberrant factors being present in double dose in the material used for inbreeding. *The only way to get rid of such material is not to stop inbreeding, but to continue it more intensively until all the scum has found its way to the surface and been skimmed off. Or else, of course, to discard the aberrant stock entirely. . . .*'

'Out-Crossing and Line Breeding

'Inbreeding reduces variability and makes for uniformity. Sometimes it may build up a uniformity like a prison wall with the genes inside as prisoners: as inbreeding is continued the genes can group together among themselves but have no contact with other genes in the outside world. The faculty for self-breeding produced by continued inbreeding is the prison wall which confines the genes.

'We may find it necessary to bring back within the walls genes which have escaped before the coping stones were put on; or to introduce genes that have never been inside. Or else we want to remove an obnoxious prisoner gene. The way in which we break down the prison wall so laboriously built is by out-crossing. The unfortunate thing is that we cannot control the exact type and number of intruders throught the breach we make in our prison wall, nor can we be certain that some of the model prisoners we wish to retain will not escape while the wall is down.

'In straightforward language and forgetting the flowers—out-crossing is an evil—sometimes a necessary evil. The object of animal breeding for utility is to make the group self-breeding for the inherited make-up of the best individuals; out-crossing destroys self-breeding and reintroduces mixed-breeding individuals. We may get the factor we want, but we shall undoubtedly get a number of factors we do *not* want, and so the slow process of turning out the unwanted ones begins again.'

'Minimizing the Risks Involved in Out-Crossing

'If you are bound to out-cross, first make certain that the out-cross animal really is a self-breeder for the gene or factor you want to bring in. Next, confine the effects of the cross to a small number of the group you wish to change. The hybrid offspring must then be bred back to the pure-bred group, and from the offspring of such matings only those few which show the most improvement in the factor required should be kept.

'These few animals should again be bred back to the pure-bred group, and this procedure continued for four or five generations—more if possible.

'With the exception of animals needed for the work, those produced by the repeated back-crosses should be discarded for breeding purposes—even though their quality be above average.

'In polygamous animals no males derived from an out-cross should be used for at least four to five generations: the new genes being introduced through the female lines where the impurities they bring handcuffed to them can do less hurt. The common sense of this is obvious. A bull will spread himself quickly through the herd, but a cow can be made to confine her impurities to three or four daughters.'

'Where to go for an Out-Cross

'Where should the anxious breeder go for an out-cross? Preferably he should stay within the breed if he can locate a strain which is outstanding in the qualities needed to be introduced or improved.

'Provided the breeder knows how heredity works and what the results of his actions are likely to be, then out-crosses from other breeds may be used with success. And a breeder who has had an eye open for the need at some future time of out-crossing may have prepared his way by *line-breeding*.'

'Line Breeding

'You always find somebody who asks "What's the difference between inbreeding and line-breeding?" and there is always somebody else at hand to give a senseless though "fly" answer.

'The truth is inbreeding and line-breeding are essentially the same process. A breeder practises line-breeding who, *instead of inbreeding his whole flock or herd, inbreeds them in separate self-contained groups.* He produces parallel inbred lines.

'Then if the necessity blows up he has the chance of reintroducing genes from one parallel line to the other without recourse to a violent out-cross and with far less danger of bringing in impurities.'

'Out-Crosses and Show Points

'For utility animals the faculty for self-breeding is the main aim after quality.

'For show animals the *individual* and not the group brings home the cash: so an out-cross may introduce just that exaggeration of fancy points which will catch a judge's eye.

'But such an individual will leave a long smear of impurity behind it if bred from. Such animals are the prize-winning slugs of the utility farming world. . . .'

'Test Mating and Progeny Testing

PROGENY TESTING

'Progeny testing is a method of finding out the general efficiency of a dairy bull (for example) for producing the kind of daughters a breeder requires.

'It simply entails the registration of the performance of his female descendants. If it is not possible to take figures for all a bull's daughters then a *random* sample should be taken, say the first-born ten or twenty. *The progeny must in no way be selected* or any value the record might have will have been destroyed at the start.

'A bull's certificate to continue as pilot of the herd, to continue breeding, should be the excellence of his breeding report. The statement of his breeding value should show the number of female calves born, the number raised, the number discarded, the number of days milked of every heifer and the results in yield and butterfat.

'A proven bull is not necessarily a good bull; but a proven bull which is prepotent (that is to say " self-breeding") in the factors which make his owner's livelihood and the country's prosperity and health, is worth his weight in gold. . . .'

My first Jersey bull had three outstanding characteristics which he transmitted to every one of his daughters and a fourth hidden characteristic

17

which he carried from his dam. The first, cocked horns and a rather plain face were rather annoying and valueless, except as an indication that the old boy was transmitting something of himself consistently. The second, a colossal barrel with widely sprung ribs and deep belly were admirable for a herd such as mine fed on homegrown foods. The third, strong, squarely placed straight legs—both back and front. Neither belly nor udder will stay the pace without sound legs to carry them and to carry them a long way when the cow has to graze her own food. The fourth is of course considered the most important—a good udder—though *I* think the stomach capacity more important. A good udder is useless without the stomach capacity to fill it. Many a bad udder has produced a lot of milk through a big belly but I've had perfect udders under flat-sided barrels which have produced unbelievably poor yields.

Having found that my bull transmitted the important conformation characteristics the question was what to do about the bad head. It is usually argued by the milk-at-all-costs boys, 'Why worry about the head?' But I have found that an intelligent, though not necessarily a pretty face, denotes the ability to produce efficiently. I have never known a cow which is an efficient milk-producer to have an unintelligent face, which may sound a tall story to the man who hasn't spent as long as I have looking cows in the face, and who may consider all cows' faces patently dumb anyhow. But I suggest, if you have an eye for an animal which looks deeper than first impressions, that you make a study of the heads of your best milking cows, and particularly the cows which are known to be efficient converters of food into milk. You may think that milk production to a cow is an automatic process, which is little or not at all affected by her state of mind or her standard of intelligence, but I am convinced that the profitable utilization of food, and the efficient conversion of food into milk, requires a special kind of intelligence in the cow which places it well above the average intelligence of its species, and that this special intelligence is observable in the facial expression of the cow. For further confirmation of this theory compare the faces of beef animals with those of milk-producing animals. Getting fat doesn't require much intelligence, and the process of becoming fat has a dulling effect on the intellect. It may be a fine point, but to the successful breeder it is an important one. Further, I had to look my cows in the face every day! My next step then was to decide whether I should try to eliminate this undesirable characteristic or to concentrate upon the good factors. It was as yet too early to say whether sufficient milk had been transmitted, or whether the bull had improved on the progeny's dam's yields of milk and butterfat. As far as production transmission was concerned, I felt that given big barrels, sound legs and good udder it was safe to assume milk—and this assumption in all my breeding, buying and judging of cattle has never failed me. It is on such experience that I disagree with the milk-and-water wallahs who say that showing is a waste of time, and that it is impossible to judge a cow's productive capacity merely by looking at her.

I decided that the way to deal with the problem of eliminating the undesirable head, while at the same time retaining the good bodies, legs and udders, was to follow the old bull with his own son out of a cow with the same good body but a more attractive head.

I found that this worked perfectly. I retained and indeed fixed all the old bull's good characteristics and yet improved the quality and intelligence of the head. By this time it was clear that the old bull's first daughters were milking well enough for my requirements, had those excellent bodies, legs and udders and the butterfat was in most cases held, though in one or two cases there was a drop in butterfat. But what was clear was that they had not quite the quality of bone which is necessary in a Jersey which is to be an efficient converter of food into milk. Coarse bone always seems to need rather more flesh to cover it than fine bone, and the tendency was with these daughters of old Top Sergente to need rather more in the way of maintenance ration than I had needed for their dams—though they were all better yielders.

It is a good thing to have big-bodied, large capacity bellies on strong legs, which are essential prerequisites of the efficient food-converting cow, but it is no use achieving that type of cow with coarse bones, for she will only want to cover them, and also use some of the valuable milk-making ingredients of her food for bone maintenance.

So I had to find an outcross which would bring quality to the bone without losing the stomach capacity—strong straight legs and shapely udders. It must, as well, be a strain that would increase the butterfat.

In my now burning enthusiasm for the Jersey cow, I had seen many herds both in the Island and in England. But one herd stood out on its own for consistency of pleasing type and butterfat. That was the Lockyers herd of John G. Bell. I went back to see that herd (after visiting others in the intervals between visits to Lockyers) so often that I came to know quite intimately many of its members, and each time I was impressed with the superiority in quality and uniformity over all other herds. The herd had been most studiously bred for over thirty years and some of the old families, two in particular, which emanated from one bull—Valentino, gave me my first real feeling of certainty regarding perfection in a Jersey. These families were founded with Lockyers Madeline and Lockyers Verbena. What they had in addition to the essential commercial and constitutional qualities which Top Sergente had given me, were a beautiful mahogany red colour, and longevity. The first, a factor which is superficially quite unimportant in the commercial dairy herd, but which influences every breeder, farmer or herdsman who loves his cows, and may even have some bearing on milk colour and fat content; the second, perhaps the most needed factor in our dairy herds to-day. So it was to the old Lockyers family that I went for bulls, and it was from the same herd, with the addition of some components from my imagination and the Top Sergente family, that I developed in my mind's eye the model of a perfect Jersey, the model which must be permanently engraved in the waking and sleeping thoughts of all keen breeders. I suppose this picture will live in my mind until one day hence in my doddering nineties I may see it grazing my pastures!

This mental picture in the heart and mind of the true breeder, is the only sound basis of genetics. And this is really what I mean when I say the genetics of animal breeding can never be learned from a book. If you haven't the ability to conjure up each time you look at a cow or a bull, the background canvas of the perfect animal against which to measure it, then you may as well decide that you had better remain a cowkeeper or a cowman only, and leave breeding and herdsmanship to those with the heart and mind for it.

There is much still to be learned about the effect of environment on breeding. Whether characteristics caused by environment can be inherited is still an open question. No book on cattle breeding gives any importance to this subject but my experience leads me to believe that acquired characteristics may be transmissible.

I was first given to consider this point when I started breeding Channel Island cattle. I soon discovered that there was a distinct island type, peculiar to animals bred on the islands. With Jerseys two characteristics were marked in animals born on the island, and the first few generations of their progeny bred away from the island. These characteristics are fine bone and the tendency to weak hocks and hind legs generally. Jerseys bred in England, with a long ancestry of English breeding have not retained such fine bone though still much finer than other breeds; neither do they have the marked tendency to 'cow hocks' which is evident in imported and early generations from imported Jerseys.

When I first went over to Jersey I found that fine bone and weak hocks were unquestionably the result of environment. The custom in the island of tying up their animals from the first few weeks of age for the rest of their lives, with little or no exercise other than being led out to tether in the summer, makes weak hocks inevitable, especially in conjunction with the so-called 'scientific starvation' which is practised to ensure fine bone.

But what struck me as remarkable, was the fact that these characteristics, particularly the weak hocks, are transmitted to their progeny bred in England and reared under perfect conditions of nutrition and exercise. I searched in vain for some mention in books on genetics of this undesirable demonstration of acquired characteristics becoming hereditary. I had pre-viously believed that weak hocks were caused solely by faulty nutrition and lack of exercise, and that it was a factor which could not be trans-mitted. But there is no doubt that in this instance, at any rate, environ-mental conditions have changed inheritance to such an extent as to render the characteristic transmit-table. In other words, we can by environment improve or harm the future inheritance of our herds. We already know that it is useless to expect breeding to overcome bad management. Because a bull whose dam has given 2,000 gallons of milk is mated to a 2,000-gallon cow it does not follow that the progeny will also give 2,000 gallons of milk at maturity. If environment is unsuitable and management is faulty, they may not give more than 200 gallons. Similarly it is probably possible by improved management and ideal environment to produce over the genera-tions, better-yielding and more profitable cattle, and in so doing influence the inheritance of characteristics acquired by good management and the right environment.

There have been many examples of cows under identical management and apparently identical feeding showing inexplicable improvement when moved from one farm to another. I recently visited a Jersey herd which had been moved from Southern Ireland to England. Cows which had never averaged more than 600 gallons of milk suddenly, under a regime identi-cal in every respect, even with exactly the same staff, poured out a herd average of 1,100 gallons. A similar capacity has been passed to the first daughters of these cows born and so far recorded in this country.

Though I have read none of his writings or even seen any published details of his theories, I understand that a Russian scientist, Dr. Lysenko, has founded a whole theory of genetics on the idea that qualities acquired by environment are inherited. My own knowledge of the subject is merely that of a breeder, but I do suggest that further serious investigation of the effect of environment on heredity is desirable. For instance, if the Island of

Jersey authorities would admit into Jersey cattle of several generations of English breeding with strong straight legs we could see if in the course of a few generations, under the conditions which have produced weak-hocked Jerseys, they would revert to cow-hocks.

All farmers know of instances of animals which have been started well by their breeder, being sold as perfect specimens of their breed, only to go back under bad management and appear later at any rate, to be thoroughly poor specimens of the breed and under the same bad environments to breed animals which appear to have inherited the characteristics created by the bad management of the dam.

Yet without knowledge of these environmental factors it would be impossible to say whether the poor specimen was the result of heredity or the effect of management of the dam before and during pregnancy. The desirable qualities of bone and horn structure in the Scottish Blackface ram can be produced artificially by suckling the young tup on a goat. The buyer believes he has found a ram with outstanding inheritance and pays an exaggerated price only to find that these qualities are not transmitted to their progeny, having been acquired in the ram purely by virtue of the greater milking capacity and richer milk of his goat foster-mother.

But would it be possible by repeating this system of ram rearing for generations to develop the ability to transmit improved bone and horns? I really don't know, and I don't know anyone who has pursued the subject long enough to find out. There is a good deal of evidence either way and I am certainly not qualified to do more than instance the above illustrations from my very limited and unscientific observations as a practical breeder.

Chapter 4

HERD EFFICIENCY

Sources of Increased Profitability

Most breeders of pedigree cattle have reached a stage in their progress towards maximum milk yields when further increases can be achieved only at the expense of the health of the animal. I believe that Breed Societies which continue to encourage the extraction of ever higher yields are merely laying the foundations of the extinction of their breeds. Sooner or later the constitution of the best milking cows will suffer and the weakness will be transmitted in ever increasing concentrations until large sections of the breed become sterile. There is bound to be a limit to the transmission of the ability to produce freak yields, particularly as the wherewithal of high milk yields *and* health, that is properly grown food, is slowly diminishing.

If a limit is to be set on higher yields, what, in the face of seemingly endless increases in costs are we to do to keep income ahead of expenditure?

There are, in my opinion, three practically untapped sources of saving: (1) Improved health in the herd. (2) Increased production efficiency, i.e. to breed for a better efficiency in the cow's ability to convert food into milk. (3) To breed for longevity. These are all sources of increased income or economy which have been largely ignored in our efforts to get more and more milk to the almost complete exclusion of any other policy.

We hear various figures from £50 million to £250 million a year quoted as the cost of disease to the dairy farmers of this country. If the figure is somewhere between the two it means that each dairy farmer in this country could be handed something like £1,000 a year if cattle diseases cost the nation nothing, without taking any account whatever of the increased income which a disease-free herd could bring to the dairy farmer.

Cattle disease is not inevitable as I have shown in my own herd, simply by adopting the commonsense organic methods described in *Fertility Farming*. The sooner the authorities accept the challenge made towards the end of this book and investigate such methods, the sooner will disease be eliminated. I expect my cows to do an average of 10 or 12 lactations with no mastitis, no sterility and no abortion and the same is possible for any farmer prepared to adopt similar methods.

Food conversion efficiency is to some extent dependent on breed. A breed which carries flesh as well as milk always draws a proportion of its food for its own body covering—and a large frame needs a larger proportion of food to maintain it than a small one. But within all breeds it is possible to select strains which are more economical converters of food into milk. The time has come for us to measure the ability of a cow, not by the quantity of milk or butterfat she gives, regardless of all other factors, but by a unit of assessment which takes account of milk total solids production in relation to body weight and food consumed. Present-day milk recording is already obsolete. A system of recording which measures cost per gallon per cwt. of body weight gives me the only true guide to profitable milk production. Such a system provided for me the information which decided me first, when I was costing three different breeds in my herd, to discard the two uneconomical breeds and concentrate on that which produced milk at the lowest cost per gallon, and second, to give up almost entirely, feeding concentrates of any kind when I found that the yield given on grass and silage was far more profitable.

Longevity, though perhaps the most important factor of all, takes longer to achieve in our policy of breeding. But if we are to farm well we must breed for longevity as well as for health and production efficiency. Fortunately longevity is often a result of the fertility farming methods about which I have written. Every farmer, if he has a good cow, wants to keep it as long as possible. So we must select good cows but good old ones are a better breeding bet than good young ones.

I own the oldest living pedigree cow—Lockyers Verbena, now 22 years old—and a grandson of hers who is also a grandson of her 18-years-old sister, both great total lifetime yielders as well as show winners. This is the breeding upon which I am concentrating. This is the blood we should all look for and concentrate in our herds.

Costs of production would then automatically fall and wastage from disease and death would be reduced to a minimum.

An excellent demonstration of the importance of milk production efficiency as distinct from merely high yields is provided by a comparison of the moderate yielding Isfield Jersey herd of Mr. F.J. Rigby. The tables on pages 27-30 show first an analysis of the milk production costs of this highly efficient Jersey herd and these costs are set alongside comparative figures for the Royal Agricultural College herds. Professor Boutflour and his deputy, Kenneth Russell, have achieved considerable fame for their methods of dairy herd management, much of which is highly creditable. Their herds have come to be regarded as the criterion of efficiency. They have put all intelligent dairy farmers on their toes and given us a measure against which to test our own herd achievements. The fact that I, and others, disagree with some of the methods employed to achieve the Royal Agricultural College results is beside the point. Whatever the methods employed, dairy farming profitability demands comparisons by final results in relation to the cost of achieving them, both in judging our methods and in choosing our breeds. Mr. Rigby has shown that a moderate yielding cow which is an efficient converter can with comparatively natural methods, emulate even the achievements of the Royal Agricultural College in profitability.

A farming friend of mine in the north is keeping about 500 cattle as well as many other animals on about 900 acres, and feeding them off the farm. I tried to persuade him to keep fewer and better cattle but he would have none of it. His theory was that if he kept valuable pedigree cattle they would only be ruined by incompetent men. Pedigree cows or reasonably high producers of any kind, he said, were only for the man who could give personal attention to his herd and thus avoid the higher loss which would result if careless treatment lost a cow.

He works on the principle that if he can get only mediocre herdsmen, then it is more profitable to attain his required milk output from large numbers instead of high-producing animals in smaller numbers. Having got his large herd he feeds them almost entirely on bulky food; gets a herd average of about 500 gallons and no disease. With herds of 250 cows in milk he has no vet's bill. He does not even produce T.T. milk so there are no charges for tests and no elaborate efforts to produce ultra-clean milk with the attendant high costs. No purchased foodstuffs, no vet's bill, no fuel bill for sterilizing utensils, no losses from disease, not even temporary infertility! I must say that though the whole of my training and instinct rebels at the idea, it does seem to work. He maintains that 250 cows averaging 500 gallons pay him better than 125 cows averaging 1,000 gallons with all the attendant troubles which are inevitable in a 1,000-gallon average herd. And the extra quantity of farmyard manure produced well repays, he claims, the cost of feeding his extra 125 cows to get the same amount of milk.

When I first looked into this friend's methods I couldn't make up my mind whether this was mass production of muck and milk which was also a sound proposition as a money producer, or whether it was just inefficient old-fashioned farming. But if it was inefficient farming, I decided, it was certainly scientific inefficiency and only careful costings will provide the right answer from the financial angle.

Unfortunately my friend points to farms where testings, recordings, costings, pedigree registering and all that paper performance associated with an attested pedigree herd, are far more costly than the value of the information they produce. So he is content to enjoy what many super-efficient farmers never see, profit in every pail of milk, without spending it all and more in finding how it got there.

There is no doubt that we have reached a stage in our milk production when the hygiene ritual is costing more than it is worth, and where much of our most costly effort in the direction of increased yield and 'improved' disease control is merely adding far more to our problems.

Vaccination against contagious abortion, for instance, about which the veterinary profession has been so confident, is now coming unstuck. Several herd owners, some well known, have already admitted that in spite of many years of vaccination with S.19 they are now experiencing a series of abortions which have no apparent explanation.

The Farmers' Weekly reported, on 26th October 1951, that its own herd which has been vaccinated with S.19 for many years, nevertheless had six abortions in succession for which no veterinary authority had been able to find an explanation. The following report appeared in *The Editor's Diary*: 'We have all been concerned over the outbreak of infertility and abortion, yet there is nothing like a little trouble at home to make one realize just how difficult a subject it is and how little is really known about it.

'A disturbance of the normal breeding cycle in our own herd at Grove Farm has brought us face to face with a trouble as puzzling as it is sudden. Previously, we have had no serious difficulty, and we have always had our stock vaccinated with S.19.

'The blow came when six autumn cows in succession either aborted within a period of up to one month, or produced dead calves at the normal time. In all these cases the calves appeared fully formed, and there were no obvious symptoms of abnormality either before or after calving.

'After a negative blood test, we ruled out contagious abortion. Other infectious causes, such as trichamoniasas and vibrio foetus, were already eliminated for obvious reasons. This left three other possibilities— heredity (eliminated in our case on the analysis of the pedigree), some unknown deficiency or—less likely—poison.

SOURCES OF INCREASED PROFITABILITY

ANALYSIS OF RESULTS OF SIX GROUPS OF FARMS FOR YEAR ENDED 1ST OCTOBER 1950 IN A MILK COSTS INVESTIGATION BY WYE COLLEGE

Group	I	II	III	IV	V	VI	New-house Farm Is-field—F. J. Rigby
Range of Cost (per gallon)	Under to 20.99d.	21.00d. to 22.99d.	23.00d. to 24.99d.	25.00d. to 26.99d.	27.00d. to 28.99d.	29.00d. and Over	
No. of Farms	11	4	11	10	3	11	
Average No. of cows per herd	31.0	28.6	33.0	24.3	29.0	27.0	**74.5**
Average yield per cow—gals.	779	791	717	687	806	663	**645**
Per cent yield: *Winter*	48.60	49.50	49.04	48.53	51.85	49.57	**40.81**
Summer	51.40	50.50	50.96	51.47	48.15	50.43	**59.19**
Per cent cows dry	21.4	19.4	17.4	19.6	16.8	16.4	**19.0**
Cost per gallon: Purch. foods	*d.* 6.89	*d.* 4.30	*d.* 6.64	*d.* 6.15	*d.* 8.04	*d.* 5.98	*d.* **3.89**
Home-grown hay, etc.	4.03	5.56	6.58	6.62	5.54	9.28	**4.22**
Grazing	1.76	1.22	1.39	2.12	2.16	2.49	**2.15**
Total Foods	12.68	11.08	14.61	14.89	15.74	17.75	**10.26**
less F.Y.M.	0.25	0.22	0.24	0.32	0.32	0.28	**0.22**
Net cost of foods	12.43	10.86	14.37	14.57	15.42	17.47	**10.04**
Labour	5.32	7.56	6.01	6.36	6.53	9.36	**5.68†**
Depreciation on cows	0.35†	0.21†	0.15†	0.82	0.92	0.09	**0.42**
Sundries	2.92	3.65	3.55	4.34	4.71	5.27	**3.22**
Net cost per gal.	20.32	21.86	23.78	26.09	27.58	32.19	**18.52**
Net cost per cow	£ 66.0	£ 72.1	£ 71.0	£ 74.7	£ 92.7	£ 88.9	£ **49.8**

† Appreciation.

Note: All figures are weighted averages. No allowance has been made for: (*a*) delivery costs of any kind; (*b*) interest on capital; (*c*) managerial salary.

The Isfield Jersey herd sold 645 gallons per cow, sold at 4s. 6d. per gallon (farm-bottled, wholesale) = £145 2s. 6d. Net cost per cow = £49 16s. Showing a margin per cow of £95 6s. 6d., excluding items (*a*), (*b*) and (*c*).

27

HERD EFFICIENCY

ANALYSIS OF RESULTS OF SIX GROUPS OF FARMS FOR YEAR ENDED 1ST OCTOBER 1950 IN A MILK COSTS INVESTIGATION BY WYE COLLEGE

2006 Currency*

Group		I	II	III	IV	V	VI	New-house Farm Isfield— F. J. Rigby
Range of Cost	£	<2.07	2.07-2.27	2.27-2.47	2.47-2.66	2.66-2.86	2.86+	Isfield— F. J.
(per gallon)	$	3.81	3.81-4.18	4.18-4.54	4.54-4.89	4.89-5.26	5.26+	Rigby
No. of Farms		11	4	11	10	3	11	
Cost per gallon: Purch. foods	£	0.68	0.42	0.65	0.61	0.79	0.59	0.38
	$	1.25	0.77	1.20	1.12	1.45	1.09	0.70
Home-grown hay, etc.	£	0.40	0.55	0.65	0.65	0.68	0.55	0.42
	$	0.74	1.01	1.20	1.20	1.25	1.01	0.77
Grazing	£	0.17	0.12	0.13	0.21	0.21	0.25	0.21
	$	0.31	0.22	0.24	0.39	0.39	0.46	0.39
Total Foods	£	1.25	1.09	1.44	1.47	1.55	1.75	1.01
	$	2.30	2.01	2.65	2.70	2.93	3.22	1.86
less F.Y.M.	£	0.02	0.02	0.02	0.03	0.03	0.03	0.02
	$	0.04	0.04	0.04	0.06	0.06	0.06	0.04
Net cost of foods	£	1.23	1.07	1.42	1.44	1.52	1.72	0.99
	$	2.26	1.97	2.61	2.65	2.80	3.16	1.82
Labour	£	0.52	0.75	0.59	0.63	0.64	0.92	0.56
	$	0.96	1.38	1.09	1.16	1.18	1.69	1.03
Depreciation on cows	£	0.03	0.02	0.01	0.08	0.09	0.01	0.04
	$	0.06	0.04	0.02	0.15	0.17	0.02	0.07
Sundries	£	0.29	0.36	0.36	0.43	0.47	0.52	0.32
	$	0.53	0.66	0.66	0.79	0.86	0.96	0.59
Net cost per gal.	£	2.01	2.16	2.35	2.58	2.75	3.17	0.79
	$	3.70	3.97	4.32	4.75	5.00	5.83	1.45
Net cost per cow	£	1,563	1,707	1,681	1,768	2,195	2,105	1,179
	$	2,875	3,140	3,093	3,254	4,038	4,001	2,170

*Editor's note: The author's historic financial data was converted to modern currencies and approximately adjusted for inflation, using the consumer price index. This most certainly will not correlate to modern costs and prices, but should be utilized for general directional trends only.

COMPARATIVE COSTINGS
PROFESSOR BOUTFLOUR'S HERDS: STEADINGS
AND FOSSEHILL, CIRENCESTER 1949 COMPARED
WITH ISFIELD PEDIGREE JERSEYS HERD

Management	Steadings Intensive	Fosse Hill Extensive	Isfield Extensive
Size of farm	64 acres	160 acres	**287 acres**
Size of herd	19 cows	38 cows	**74½ cows**
Breed	Friesian	Ayrshire	**Jersey**
System	Shed and Hand Milking	Yards and Parlour	**Shed, Yards and Parlour**
Gross sale, milk	1,090 gallons £147 per cow	660 gallons £96 per cow	**645 gallons £147 per cow**
Gross cost, milk	£74 10 0	£58	**£49 16 0**
	£ s. d.	£ s. d.	**£ s. d.**
Food, home-grown	22 18 0	19 4 0	**11 7 0**
Graze	6 10 0	6 9 0	**5 15 6**
Purchased	14 2 0	7 14 0	**10 9 0**
Total	43 0 0	33 0 0	**27 11 6**
Labour total	£24	£12 8 0	**£15 5 0**
Misc. and Depreciation	£7 10 0	£12 12 0	**£8 7 0**
Profit margin per cow	£72 10 0	£38 0 0	**£95 6 6**
Returns per £100 food cost	£340 0 0	£310 0 0	**£540 0 0**
Returns per £100 labour	£650 0 0	£777 0 0	£1,080 0 0
Returns per £100 cow capital	£210 0 0	£160 0 0	£145 0 0

Steadings and **Fosse Hill herds** are **T.T. attested,** in process of grading up.
Isfield herd is full pedigree island foundation stock, **T.T. attested**, closed herd.
The **Isfield production** is sold to Uckfield Dairies Limited (same owner as the herd) at farm-bottled standard price.
The **Isfield herd** and **Steadings** have identical cash sales of £147 each,
Steadings with 1,090 gallons, **Isfield** with 645 gallons only per cow.

HERD EFFICIENCY

CIRENCESTER 1949
COMPARED WITH ISFIELD PEDIGREE JERSEYS HERD
2006 Currency*

Management		Steadings Intensive	Fosse Hill Extensive	Isfield Extensive
Size of farm		64 acres	160 acres	**287 acres**
Size of herd		19 cows	38 cows	**74½ cows**
Breed		Friesian	Ayrshire	**Jersey**
System		Shed and Hand Milking	Yards and Parlour	**Shed, Yards and Parlour**
Gross sale, milk		1,090 gallons	660 gallons	**645 gallons**
	£	3,587.06	2,342.57	**3,587.06**
	$	6,600.19	4,310.33	**6,600.19**
Gross cost, milk	£	1,817.93	1,415.30	**1,215.21**
	$	3,344.99	2,604.15	**2,235.99**
Food, home-grown	£	558.80	468.51	**276.96**
	$	1,028.19	862.06	**509.61**
Graze	£	158.61	157.39	**140.92**
	$	291.84	289.60	**259.29**
Purchased	£	344.06	187.89	**255.00**
	$	633.07	345.72	**469.20**
Total	£	1,049.28	805.26	**672.88**
	$	1,930.68	1,481.68	**1,238.10**
Labour total	£	585.64	302.58	**372.13**
	$	1,077.58	556.75	**684.72**
Misc. & Depreciation	£	183.01	307.46	**203.75**
	$	336.74	565.73	**374.90**
Profit margin per cow	£	1,769.13	927.27	**2,326.10**
	$	3,255.14	1,706.18	**4,280.02**
Returns per £100 food cost	£	8,296.60	7,564.55	**13,176.95**
	$	15,265.74	13,918.77	**24,245.59**
Returns per £100 labour	£	15,861.15	18,960.17	**26,353.90**
	$	29,184.52	34,886.71	**48,491.18**
Returns per £100 cow capital	£	5,124.37	3,904.28	**3,538.26**
	$	9,428.84	7,183.88	**6,510.40**

Editor's note: The author's historic financial data was converted to modern currencies and approximately adjusted for inflation, using the consumer price index. This most certainly will not correlate to modern costs and prices, but should be utilized for general directional trends only.

'Fortunately, subsequent calvings have been normal, and there is some comfort anyway in the fact that the earlier calvings were predominantly bull calves. We are also managing to get some milk out of the affected cows, so that they are not a complete loss.

'Nevertheless, the trouble is a serious one and both the veterinary profession and we want to get to the bottom of it. It would be interesting and helpful to hear of any similar trouble occurring on other farms.'

The explanation to me seems obvious. S.19 was given the credit for a respite from abortion which follows an outbreak in any herd. The act of abortion is itself a curative process, without which an animal managed by orthodox methods would otherwise become sterile. The only permanent preventive of abortion, or any other cattle disease for that matter, is a complete revolution in management which necessitates a natural nutrition, of the soil, the calf and the cow, in that order of importance: If the soil is healthy, all the animals on the farm have a better chance of health through the home-grown food which I believe to be an essential to proper health. If the calf is naturally fed then the chances of a healthy cowhood are made safe. Then, assuming we *still* insist on over-exploiting the cow she has a better chance of surviving our treatment. But to expect a cow to withstand modern milk production on unnatural food without the health foundations of a reasonably natural calfhood is asking too much.

Chapter 5

A CALL FOR SOME
CATTLE-SALE REFORMS
and a Formula for Future Sales

Though average prices of pedigree cattle to-day are settling down to a reasonable level, record prices are still being made for all breeds of pedigree cattle; buyers have apparently never been so keen to pay for good stock, and yet it still needs a brave man to gamble his money in the pedigree saleyard.

For gamble indeed it is in many cases. Any man who has bought stock at collective sales of pedigree cattle in recent years will speak with deep feeling when the subjects of udder warranties, tuberculin tests, and shy breeding are mentioned.

In spite of modern safeguards and the admirable trend of some pioneers towards the frank catalogue, I am not alone when I say that I always experienced a weakness about the knees for some days after a purchase at a pedigree sale. Snags are still far more common than pleasant surprises when the new cow is put to a working test at home.

The so-called udder warranty is perhaps the greatest culprit. Some of my own experiences in buying illustrate the anomalies of present sale rules in this respect and will, I hope, show how the udder warranty conditions could give a fairer deal to the buyer without bringing any hardship on the reputable vendor.

I have bought cows with udders and teats warranted sound, but which have not survived the journey home in good order.

Against this there is no protection and apparently no possibility of redress.

The rules of several breed societies contain a clause requiring a guarantee that any cow in-calf or in-milk, or any heifer in-milk, is sound in udder and teats at the time of sale, but admitting no claim in respect thereof which is not made within one hour of the close of the sale.

To expect anyone to give a sound judgment on the condition of an udder that has been stocked for eighteen hours, in the harassing conditions of the average saleyard is, of course, fantastic. The cow must be got home and given at least two milkings before she can fairly be judged in the udder.

I have closely examined the udders of cows I was intending to buy. Where there has been only slight suspicion of thickening in the milk passage, or a little lightness in one quarter, and I have particularly liked the cow, I have taken the risk.

In any case, I was then experimenting on my treatment for mastitis and was satisfied that I could cure them if they did go wrong.

Surely enough, some have gone wrong. I have had cows with a suspicion of thickening in the udder before the sale, but which, confident in the udder warranty, I have purchased, only to find them giving filthy milk at the first milking on arrival home. Others that I suspected to be slightly light in one quarter, have gone wrong in that quarter within a few days of arrival home.

That I was able to treat them does not alter the fact that such cases do not give a square deal to the buyer. For cost of treatment is not anticipated in the purchase of expensive pedigree cattle.

Expert examination has sometimes revealed obvious cases of longstanding mastitis which had presumably been treated and rendered temporarily ineffective. The trouble remained dormant only to break out under the strain of stocking the udder, followed by a long train journey.

Where complaints have been made immediately the cattle were home, the auctioneers naturally reminded me of the 'conditions of sale'. The reputation of vendors proves to be no safeguard. When complaints are passed to them, they merely need affirm that the udders were sound when they left the farm or the saleyard, and their responsibility is ended, unless legal action is taken and misrepresentation proved.

What is the buyer to do in such a case? It is surely wrong that all the burden of such a loss should be on the unfortunate buyer, who, in such cases, cannot possibly have any part in the causation of the udder trouble.

Conditions of sale ruling at most auctions to-day encourage the breeder to use them for the disposal of his duds. If the cattle can survive the hour after the sale the vendor has succeeded in passing his dud and the buyer has no redress. If the buyer were allowed to have the cow on his farm for just one day there would be reasonable time to give the udder a working test and place the blame for any defect where it rightly belongs.

Complaints arising from such a procedure would react unfavourably only on the habitual seller of unsound udders. For udders do not suddenly become rotten with mastitis overnight. Any outbreak of mastitis within twenty-four hours of a sale is certain to have existed in the udder at the time of, or before the sale. It is therefore reasonable that the seller, not the buyer, should be the loser, or at least share the loss.

In any case most mastitis is of deeper seated origin than the mere mechanical infection by external bacteria, and cases such as I have described are almost certain to be the result of previous bad management, or breeding which has predisposed the animal to mastitis.

Many young farmers are starting new pedigree herds at the present time and breed societies would do well to turn their attention to the satisfaction of these newcomers, instead of watching mainly the interests of their council members who are normally all established vendors themselves.

Present prices of livestock are quite high enough to allow for any financial disadvantage likely to result for the vendor from a change of sale rules. Buyers of pedigree stock at least deserve sound stock, if not value for money, in return for the abnormally high prices which some of them have had to pay in recent years. Under existing sale rules, high prices are not the guarantee of sound stock that one would expect them to be.

How can this state of affairs be made more equitable?

There are two modifications of present conditions of sale which would go a long way towards levelling the balance of risk between vendor and buyer, and so help to eliminate the disgruntled buyer who can be no advertisement to any breed society.

(1) An extension of the time allowed for the lodging of complaints to at least twenty-four hours (or alternatively the length of time necessary to enable the buyer to get the cow home and milk her at least once).

(2) The prohibition of udder stocking, making it illegal for a cow to be left unmilked for more than six hours before the sale.

Even such small changes as I have suggested take a long, long time. For most breed societies are governed entirely by the vendor member. In the meantime the newcomer is buying trouble.

There is one simple safeguard which will help the buyer to avoid buying mastitis. If a few small pieces of bromochresol paper (available from any chemist's shop) are carried to the sale and a drop of the milk—or pre-calving 'honey'—from each quarter of any cow which may be purchased is tested on the paper—udder trouble can be detected before it is evident to the human eye. Such a simple precaution may save the expense and trouble of litigation which is the only way of redress when udder trouble is not detected before the cow leaves the saleyard.

The foregoing criticism of buying pitfalls applies mainly to England and Wales. Conditions of sale, I am told, in most parts of Scotland gives almost unfair advantage to the buyer over the vendor, or exposer as he is called north of the border.

Perhaps this explains the rapid spread of the Ayrshire; for it is possible to buy a newly calved cow, get her home to the south of England, and have a day in which to test her udder before complaints need be registered.

It will show the example which our breed societies need, if I quote some of the conditions of sale prevailing in the south-west of Scotland.

Firstly, the condition relating to udder warranty, which is the one which gives most cause for complaint in our English pedigree sales:

'Calved cows and heifers. *Purchasers must intimate, in writing, to the Auctioneers within three days of purchase any complaint as to the vessel or teats ...*'

This warranty not only relates to the condition of the teats and udder, but to the quietness of the cow to milk. How some of our wartime milking staffs would have been glad of cows coming into the herds under such a warranty of quietness.

The following is the rule taken from the catalogue of a show and sale held at Annan, Dumfriesshire:

'*Animals sold for dairy purposes, heifers carrying first calf excepted, shall be held to be warranted by the exposer as correct in their vessels, and teats and quiet to milk unless mention shall be made at the time of sale to the contrary.*'

The warranty even extends to cows that have not yet calved. This means that it is possible to buy a cow before calving, at a stage when it is difficult to judge the likely condition of the udder after calving, and to have an assurance of the soundness of her udder up to three days after calving. The rule reads:

'Calving Cows. *Complaints of unsoundness of vessel and teats must be made, in writing,* not later than three days after calving, *to the Auctioneers.*'

If there is a breed society in England, with sale rules that offer a guarantee of udder soundness with an in-calf animal, that extends to three days after calving, then I would like to know of it.

Credit is certainly due to the man who has the courage to sell cows with such refreshing assurance. For the practice is all too common of cows that have given trouble in a previous lactation being offered for sale a short time before they are due to calve, at a time when it is difficult for an expert, let alone a newcomer to pedigree cattle buying, to detect a faulty udder.

So that there shall be no uncertainty about the safeguards which are insisted upon by the auctioneers in these Scottish sales, the warranty is further elaborated in the following rule:

'Back Calvers and Spring Calvers. *All animals sold as such are warranted in-calf and correct in their vessels unless otherwise stated. Exposers must intimate to the Auctioneers at the time of sale if the animal is still milking. No claim will be entertained unless any complaint is intimated in writing to the auctioneers by the purchaser, in respect of animals giving milk*, within three days after date of sale *and in respect of dry animals* three days after calving.'

What a pleasure it must be to buy udders with such guarantee of soundness; for it is the udder after all which is paid for. A cow with one bad quarter is less than half a cow, and a cow with two bad quarters is no cow at all!

The breed society that will give England a lead by following this admirable example of Scottish straightforwardness will earn the heartfelt gratitude of hundreds of bewildered cattle buyers, who are attending the pedigree cattle sales to-day, money in hand, prepared to pay high prices for really sound stock, but who too often come home to find they have bought a good looker with useless 'tackle'.

Newcomers to pedigree cattle breeding will never succeed on good looks and it will be no more than our English breed societies have deserved if buyers continue to go, in increasing numbers, over the border for their foundation stock.

I know from the letters I have had on this subject that buyers will flock to the first breed society sale that has courage enough to give fair safeguard to the comparative novice (and indeed the hardened veteran too, for even he buys trouble sometimes). And nothing short of the conditions I have quoted from Scotland, will constitute fair safeguard. What we really need, at any rate for pedigree animals entered for sale, is an official 'passport' which records the history of the animal. Farmers are so burdened with bookkeeping and records to day that I hesitate to suggest the addition of another. But it would bring such immense benefit to all cattle breeders, that I do urge breed societies to support and actively campaign for its adoption. My suggestion is simple. It is that a life history pedigree form of a type I designed for my own use some years ago, should be entered in the appropriate place on the back by the vet. himself each time he visits a cow, including tuberculin tests (with measurements). Instead of the usual registration certificate issued by breed societies a life history form should be devised and issued on official registration. The extended pedigree with milk records of all females in the pedigree should be shown on one side and on the other, provision for all details in the life of the animal, including every visit of the vet, all milk records with calving dates and all changes of ownership.

When breed societies do perform this necessary service for the buyer, what is going to happen to the doubtful cows that are to-day being offered at pedigree sales?

Well, mastitis can be cured now, simply and surely by the farmer or herdsman himself by the method described on page 122 of this book. There is therefore certainty of bringing a cow back to full milk providing the udder has not been structurally damaged. I am prepared to buy cows suffering from mastitis, providing I know what I am buying and providing the purchase price takes account of the likely cost of treatment.

Therefore why not institute a separate section of the sales for cows that cannot be fully guaranteed in the udder and later for cows which have no life history card. Buyers can then approach the saleyard with complete confidence and pay to the giddy limits of price records for fully warranted cattle and sleep peacefully on the return home in the knowledge that real milk will flow from the udder for the next few weeks at least.

Or buyers can go to the non-guaranteed section and buy at a reasonable price good breeding animals that may be brought home and treated, at a cost that will fall fairly on the vendor and the purchaser.

Is it asking too much that complete confidence should take the place of what amounts to confidence trickery in many cattle sale-yards to-day?

There is still one grave crime in my opinion, which even the Scots have not eradicated, which a life history card could not prevent, and which must be wiped out if udders are to be fairly warranted, and indeed protected against future trouble. That is udder stocking.

It is no doubt this practice which is at the root of most udder trouble which immediately follows with animals that have passed through a saleyard. The vendor is blamed for passing off an animal with mastitis, whereas the real culprits are those who fail to prohibit this unnecessary cruelty to the cow as well as to the buyer.

What we need now, is just one auctioneer or breed society with the bold-ness to open a sale under the rules quoted above, with the addition of a rule prohibiting the stocking of udders for more than six hours. Such an action would be well repaid, in more ways than cash. It has been tried once, at my instigation, but only locally. Will a brave breed society follow on where the story below finishes?

I found a firm of auctioneers interested in establishing complete confidence among its customers, and they were responsible for organizing sales in which we had conditions at any rate, approaching a fair deal for all concerned.

Six years ago as the first Chairman of the South-Western Jersey Breeders' Club I took part in the organization of what I believe was the first sale in the world, at which all in-milk animals were completely milked out before going into the sale ring. This was a Show and Sale, so we were able to give buyers and judges an opportunity of seeing the cows with their udders full, for they were first paraded at 9 a.m. (having been milked out the previous evening), were examined by the judges, then milked out, before the judge made his final placings. This example was followed somewhat half-heartedly, I regret to say, by two breed societies since, yet it is surprising how often a judge has to change the order of placings after the milk has been removed from the udder and it is possible really to examine it unstocked and in the raw.

Our first example gave much confidence to buyers, and removed some of the dangers of damage to the udder resulting from overstocking. Prices realized reflected the support for the effort to establish buyer-confidence.

In September 1950 another Jersey sale was held at Bristol by the same auctioneers, which, in addition to this milking-out condition added even higher standards and went as far as to guarantee the udder for a period of twenty-four hours after the sale (something which I had urged for years but never before achieved), and the complete health of the animal as far as a veterinary surgeon was able to assess beforehand. Minimum production standards far higher than anything ever before set were a condition of entry, and each animal was examined by two prominent judges, Mr. Eric Boston, of the Wilcote herd, and Mr. Bob Carson, of Jersey, who rejected any animal which was not of good Jersey type.

All cows had to have produced at least 450 lb. of butterfat, and bulls were accepted only from dams which had given 525 lb. of fat in a lactation of 305 days. Every animal carried a veterinary certificate of health and had passed the tuberculin test, being from attested herds only, and the agglutination test, showing that it was free from the abortion bacillus.

Support was forthcoming from breeders in all parts of the country with entries of 50 head. A big company of buyers from a wide area filled the sale yard.

1. Coming in for milking. S. Mayall's Pimhill herd which is managed
on lines advocated by the author.

2. Long-lived families which have bred consistently are the best source of foundation
stock. Five generations in the Ayrshire herd of S. Mayall. Pimhill Sarah heads
a family line.

3. The author with one of his prize-winning cows and her twenty-minute-old calf.
A healthy cow takes calving in her stride.

4. Mr. Newman Turner with the newly born calf of a fifteen-year-old Jersey cow in his
herd. Good old cows make reasonably priced foundation stock.

A FORMULA FOR FUTURE SALES

At a time when the market had been flooded with Jersey cattle and there had been as many as four or five major sales of Jersey cattle in a week with prices in general at their lowest for many years, public support for the continuation of such special selective sales was indicated in a higher average price than had previously been realized in the south-west of England.

The buyer of pedigree cattle is obviously prepared to pay more for animals which can be guaranteed in every way, which he knows he can take home with reasonable certainty of continued health and productive ability; which hitherto we breeders must admit he has not always been able to do in the past.

Mr. A. R. Taylor, of Yeovil, the auctioneer, is to be congratulated on his repeated efforts to raise the standards of pedigree cattle sales. (Since I wrote the above Mr. Taylor met a tragic death in a motor accident. It is to be hoped that someone will have the courage to carry on his good work.)

I am sure many commercial dairy farmers are deterred from 'going pedigree' by the prices quoted by the weekly farming papers of the collective sales and shows and sales of pedigree animals. I don't know whether the auctioneers themselves or the reporters commissioned by the papers are responsible for the lists of prices quoted after each sale, but the impression is given by quoting only the top prices that no reasonably priced animals are to be found at pedigree sales. The result, I feel sure, is that the commercial farmer who was never more ready to change over to pedigree cattle, just keeps away from pedigree sales and says: 'Pedigree cattle are beyond my pocket.'

While there was a good picking for the breeder-vendor, at the high prices which have been common during and since the war, no doubt the interests of breeders, auctioneers and the farming industry were being served by encouraging the people with money enough for costly animals, to spend it on pedigree cattle. The two large circulation farming weeklies were probably then justified in giving the impression that it was useless to go to a show and sale of pedigree cattle unprepared to spend 200 guineas or more for good animals. But the time has now come when to continue this false impression is doing service to nobody, least of all the vendor. There is now a strong and growing desire among working farmers to launch themselves in the pedigree cattle business. At last the 'average' farmer is convinced that it is as cheap to feed a pedigree animal as it is to feed a mongrel. If these men could know that it is possible to buy useful pedigree cows and heifers at very little more than the prices paid for good commercial attested animals, they would come to the sales at Reading and other centres and pay reasonable prices for the good yielding cow which is not quite up to breeders' standards.

I was at a Jersey Show and Sale recently at which I sat beside a working farmer. He had a milk round which he had decided to supply with farm-bottled Jersey milk. His main concern at this sale was to buy good yielding cows, regardless of their looks. No one would have believed it from the report of the sale, which listed many animals which sold for 150 guineas or more, cows which in most cases were not giving anything startling in the way of milk yields, yet my farmer friend bid his way right through the sale, never paying more than 100 guineas for a cow and by the end of the sale he had bought cows giving a total of 50 gallons of milk daily for an expenditure of £1,000. He had carefully examined all these cows before the sale and was confident that they were all sound. It is, of course, most unlikely that he avoided trouble of any kind, but at least such careful buying at those prices meant that he had little to lose, and practically every single animal would pay its purchase price and a good deal more (at 4s. 8d. a gallon for the milk) long before the end of its lactation.

The information that good milk yielders can be purchased at pedigree sales at reasonable prices has hitherto not been considered news by the farming papers. But if such stories as that of the man who bought 50 gallons of milk a day, for £1,000, at a pedigree Show and Sale and similar stories which may regularly be found at Reading and other pedigree cattle centres, were reported in the farming papers, instead of the old, old story that 500 guineas was exceeded so many times, and that Lord What's-his-name gave 2,000 guineas for a bull, the men who are looking for reasonably priced pedigree animals would roll up. The sales which have in the past tended to be social occasions for business-men-hobby farmers, might instead be opportunities for the commercial farmer to improve his herd.

Section Two

THE SHOWING AND JUDGING
OF DAIRY CATTLE

Chapter 6

HOW TO JUDGE A DAIRY COW

The chapter on genetics and breeding policy has already provided the best basis for the prospective judge of cattle. The points which I have shown to be worth breeding for in a dairy cow are obviously the points which a judge should look for in the ring. Some of the points worth breeding for are not, however, capable of assessment in the ring. Lifetime yield is one; efficiency of food conversion and freedom from disease are others. But a careful inspection of the female in the ring gives as good a guide to her potentialities as is possible. I disagree emphatically with the people who contend that shows are a waste of time and useless as a means of measuring the ability of one animal against another. British supremacy in the pedigree cattle world has been built on the improvements which the show ring has made possible. One may equally say the same of present-day official milk recording, for all that it tells us is how much milk a cow has given.

It says nothing about how much it cost to produce that milk and consequently gives no guide as to the profitability of the cow which is the main thing we want to know about a cow when we are comparing her with others. This means, then, that milk recording is an even more obscure guide than the show ring if we are to take either system separately as a means of judging a cow. A combination of milk records and inspection with added information regarding the food consumed and the cow's body weight, would provide the ideal means of judging animals. But food consumption is extremely difficult to record officially so today we must rely on the other three factors.

Even then it is possible, with the knowledge of milk and butterfat yield, to study the cow's appearance and estimate whether or not her conformation is the kind which gives milk efficiently. I am quite sure it is possible to look at a cow and say within not unreasonable limits that she is shaped, her udder is attached and the whole is supported on legs in such a way as to indicate that the milk she gives is given efficiently. The ribs alone will give a good guide on this point for no dairy cow with flesh on her ribs during a lactation can be considered an efficient milk producer. She wouldn't convert enough of her food into flesh to cover her ribs if she were.

But more often than not one is called upon to judge the animals solely on their appearance on the day of the show. So it is on appearance alone that we must discuss the way to judge a cow.

Nearly all my experience as a judge of show cattle—and certainly most of my experience in recent years—has been with Jerseys. So I can best demonstrate the judging of a dairy cow on the Jersey. I feel sure no member of any other dairy breed society will deny that whatever other failings the Jersey cow may have, she stands supreme as the perfect model of a dairy cow. Year after year the Jersey cow stands at the top of the line on inspection points at the Dairy Show in the judging for the Supreme Individual Championship (though she is generally beaten to first place in the final placing, because a cow of another breed twice as heavy has given about one-third to half as much again more milk, probably at two or three times the cost). The leading judges with any claim to impartiality are agreed on the Jersey model of symmetry, beauty and temperament upon which they would model the conformation of other breeds. On the more controversial function of milk and butterfat yields general opinion is very divided and the enthusiast of each breed has his reasons for choosing his own particular breed. I have reproduced a selection of these reasons for each dairy breed in a later part of this book.

The first thing to equip oneself with for the task of judging is a good knowledge of the official score card of the breed. I am not suggesting that in the ring it is possible or even desirable to score each animal, total up the points awarded and thus place the paraded cattle in order of merit. This may be done by a few judges—but I have never met them. I do often feel though that many official judges could do with at least a nodding acquaintance with the score card! We might then get more consistent placing of cattle and we should not suffer so often the annoyance of seeing, for example, the Royal Show Champion placed third or fourth under a different judge against the same competition at a small county show. It is, of course, quite common for a cow to be off colour one day and on top of her form the next day, for her form at the moment she is under the judge's eye to affect the final placing and to vary according to her form. But I am sure a good judge should be able to judge *through* form, and to close his eyes to the superficial sheen of the day and place the cow as a cow and not as a pretty picture. As an example of what I mean I'll illustrate with an experience we had at shows in 1950. At one show on a Monday, Dolly Daydream was awarded first prize and Treasure was given fifth place in the same class. On the Thursday of the same week and under the same judge at a different show Dolly Daydream was placed fifth and Treasure was third. When asked why—the judge said: "You spent a little more time on preparing Treasure this time." The superficial appearance of the cow had affected the placing. I do feel that the Judge's eye should have penetrated beneath the veneer of show preparations and judged the honest cow as a cow and not the skill of her owner in presenting her. He should not in my opinion have put one up and one down on the second day simply because we had applied more spit and polish, tail trimming and rugging to one than the other. A good judge should be able to place animals in their working clothes at any stage of their lactations. It is reasonable to expect a cow to be clean and fit to handle in the show ring but it should not be necessary to spend weeks of preparation and, with some breeds, keeping the animals covered with rugs. If I had my way, prizes would be withheld from any animal which is seen to wear a rug, except by permission of stewards after examination by a vet, at any time during the show. This would at any rate stop the rugging before the show, for no owner would expose a home-rugged cow in this way if at the show, he had to risk the whole day without a rug.

But here I speak only as a judge. As an exhibitor of cattle I am still compelled, in order to enable my cattle to compete fairly with other rugged cattle, to do a limited amount of rugging especially for the earlier shows in May and June. In the section of this book on preparing for show, rugging is allowed for.

But as a judge I must say I am prejudiced against animals which by their exceptional sleekness have obviously lived in rugs and also indoors for months before a show. I try to judge the animal for what it is and not for what its owner or herdsman has tried to make it appear to be. And I hope, if another judge here and there will do the same, the commercial breeder, who has neither the time, staff, money, nor inclination to coddle his cows, will at last be able to compete on equal terms with the cow-coddling pot hunter. Breed societies are always afraid of offending their successful members, who are probably responsible for making the rules anyway, by introducing such a simple, yet revolutionary rule as forbidding rugging at shows.

But judges who have the courage to discourage the 'hot-house flower' by allowing it to wilt at the bottom of the line from time to time, will do more good for agricultural shows, and their fellow breeders who have to make cows pay their way—than all the half-hearted pleas of Breed Society Councils.

My own breed, the Jersey, is the very worst offender at the larger county shows, with the use of the rug and, what is more, the back sheet or sheets. Heaven only knows how many prospective newcomers to the breed have ploughed up and down the Jersey lines weaving their way between layers of thick and almost hermetically sealed canvas curtains, vainly hoping to get a glimpse of one or two of the Jersey cows which inside these secret caverns are further shrouded with heavy woollen blankets so firmly fixed that one hardly dare lift a corner to peep at the sweltering creature panting for breath underneath, only to give it up and go to one of the breeds which are openly displayed for anyone to see without a thing to hide.

With a reasonable knowledge of the breed score card, but above all that indelible picture of the perfect cow of your dreams in your mind, one can go into the ring well equipped to place the animals in order of merit. But in support of this essential knowledge, an instinct about a correct animal, gives confidence which defies all the ringside judges and the feeling that one is judging for one's own satisfaction, selecting the animals in the order that one would admit them to one's own herd, not anyone else's. It is absolutely essential to close one's eyes to the very existence of anyone else outside the ring. Each will have his or her own idea of the best and worst animals in the ring, from where he or she is looking, and no doubt a few odd ideas about the man in the centre of the ring as well. But *you* are the only man who is looking at the animals from the inside of the ring and you are the only person qualified at that moment to place the animals correctly. You are therefore the only man whose opinion need be taken into account. Above all don't judge the man leading the cow, for if you do you may, like me, be tempted to place the cow in the hands of that ridiculously ostentatious showman lower than she deserves. Nothing irritates me more, or is more likely to make me want to go against my own better judgment of the animal, than the man who indicates with every gesture of his hands, head and backside, that *he* has already decided the order in which *you* should place them. Unfortunately some judges are influenced by the obvious showman. My own reaction is to suspect that he has something to conceal in his animal.

Standing first of all in the centre of the ring, the process of judging I prefer to follow is this. The animals come in and move clockwise around the perimeter of the ring, arranged in numerical order. I start to judge in my own mind as soon as the first animal enters the ring, unless there are other detractions such as conversation with the stewards. So the first animal in the ring gets the first, and probably the longest viewing. If the animal has any bad faults it is too bad for the exhibitor that he came in first. If the animal is really good it allows the fact to be well impressed on my mind. As the animals parade round and round, first general impressions are formed. One or two animals stand out at once as superior in general appearance and conformation. Then the animals are paraded in the opposite direction in case one side of the animal, as often is the case, is better than the other. Obvious faults such as sloping rumps, weak loins, badly shaped or sagging udders, sickle and 'cow' hocks and lameness are spotted on this first general view—and if the class is so big that some weeding out has to be done before judging proper can begin then I turn out any that have no prospect of being placed. With a big class, judging is very much simplified by starting at the bottom and eliminating the worst, before starting at the top and picking out the best.

The animals are then stopped and examined closely and individually where they stand. The aim of this first individual inspection is not so much to make comparisons as to find the less obvious faults and to make a note, mental or literal, if one or more of the animals is near faultless or obviously superior to the rest of the entries. This close inspection will eliminate one or two more hopeless cases which may be sent out of the ring at once. It is usual to ask the steward to give the instructions for animals to leave the ring and in order to 'soften' the disappointment to the adoring owner or herdsman of the rejected animal, the moment for doing this is delayed until the animals are moving round again, unless the ring is still uncomfortably overcrowded and immediate despatch of the more obvious duds is necessary to relieve pressure in the ring.

This individual examination takes note of udder shape, quality and attachment, teat placings, spring of rib, shoulder fineness, hip width, tail setting, and quality of bone generally, pliability and silkiness of skin, legs and head, and general appearance at close range. It helps to confirm or deny first impressions and detect any obvious defects which may disqualify the animal, such as overshot or undershot jaws. One may also take account of such indications of milking ability as the amount of surplus flesh, ease of milking, brightness of eye and body size in relation to udder capacity, bearing in mind that a small cow may have a proportionately greater udder capacity and in consequence is likely to produce as great a yield of milk as the next one, at a proportionately lower cost. Points cannot be awarded for such rough estimates but other things being equal, they must be taken into one's assessment.

Apart from one's own personal taste and the model of perfection in one's mind's eye, which are certain to influence the final placing, I may here go through the major important factors in the judging of a cow. Though we must accept the breed score card as the final authority if we are to achieve anything approaching a uniform breed standard, I am inclined, as I suppose are most judges, to place the emphasis regarding order of importance of the various points, rather differently. For instance, an alert movement and purposeful gait with four strong straight legs squarely placed, is the first requirement of a first prize winner. That type of animal is the one I plump for in the original general inspection and she starts with an advantage over all others. She has the frame which is necessary to support a large heavy udder and a capacious body full of food. Cow hocked or sickle hocked hind legs, or narrowly placed and knock-kneed forelegs are rejected at once in my judgment; for, good as her udder may be and correct as she may be in other respects, a cow with weak legs cannot possibly last long as a working cow, though she may survive as a hot-house show specimen, dried off early in the lactation (as soon as the show season is over) to save the shape of her udder and the strain on her legs. So, good legs must come first in my judgment.

Second in importance is the body and belly to provide the food to fill the udder. The barrel must be deep and wide across the underside. The wider the body is at the extremities of the ribs the better, indicating large stomach capacity. The whole framework of the cow must be angular and fit roughly into three triangles.

The first triangle is from front to back, i.e. from the neck as the apex and the hips as the base; the second from the top of the shoulders or chine as the apex, and the chest and forelegs as the base, and the third with the backbone as the apex and the belly as the base. The wider the base of these triangles the better in each case, indicating ample uterus capacity and spacious pelvic girdle in the first, great heart and lung capacity in the second, and large stomach capacity in the third. Similarly the finer the apex in each case the less surplus flesh the animal carries, and consequently the more efficient she is likely to be as a converter of foodstuffs into milk.

Having picked out the animals with frames that are capable of carrying them, I judge the udders.

Just as a perfect udder is useless without the strength and straightness of legs to support it, and stomach capacity to fill it, so the good body, though it does in many cases generally make the best of a bad udder, cannot be fully used without a capacious and well-shaped udder. The nearest thing we know to perfection is the udder of a good Ayrshire cow. Apart from a tendency to rather small teats, which is now being bred out of the best herds, Ayrshires have the ideal udder. The Jersey comes a very close second and some of the best Jerseys may now be emulating the Ayrshire. For

5. Milking out in the ring during judging at the Royal Dublin Show, 1947.

6. General view of the judging at an English Jersey Cattle Society's Autumn Show and Sale. Note how the good herdsman 'shows' his animal continuously but without 'showing' himself too much.

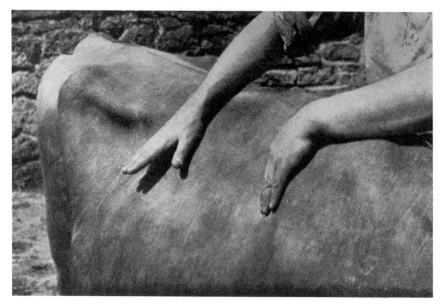

7. A good spring of rib.

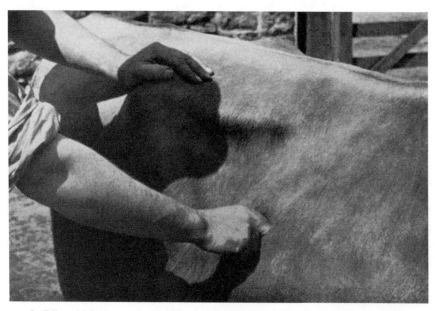

8. Ribs widely 'sprung' and wide apart. Photo shows two bent knuckles between last two ribs. Open ribs and wide space between hip and last rib indicates large stomach capacity.

nothing equals the Jersey for fineness of skin texture and the ability of the udder to milk out clean and empty.

The essentials of a good udder are that its shape should be as near to square as possible with the addition in front of an extension which runs forward under the body flush with the floor of the rest of the udder and the belly. Teats should be an even size capable of being held comfortably in one hand, placed evenly near the outer 'corners' of the udder and placed a good distance apart, ideally 6 to 9 inches according to the size of the udder. The teats should draw, i.e. be capable of being milked, easily but should not drip milk in the ring. Milk leaking from the udder indicates overstocking of the udder, or a weakness in the teats. An obviously stocked cow would be rejected by me at once. A cow with leaking teats, though she may not be disqualified, could not be placed very high.

The rear of the udder should continue vertically to the escutcheon with little or no division evident between the two rear quarters. The wider the udder is between the legs and the longer it is from back to under belly attachment the greater the capacity.

The whole impression of the udder should be as an integral part of the cow's body, rather than as an accessory to the cow which was attached separately when it became necessary for the cow to give milk. The 'built in' udder which is joined flush with the escutcheon at the back, the flanks at the sides and the belly in front is the model of perfection.

The worst faults are uneven and awkwardly placed teats; an udder which cuts up to the belly at the front or slopes forward from the escutcheon at the back; a sloppy pendulous udder or one with a bottle neck, i.e. one which is narrow at the attachment, bagging out towards the middle and the base. Such udders quickly collapse under heavy work, the muscles being unable to stand the strain of carrying large quantities of milk.

There are not many udders which show no demarcation or appearance of division between the two hind quarters. Though the udder entirely without division is superficially better looking and more acceptable to most judges, I am not sure that it is the best kind of udder. The muscle strength of the undivided udder is in my experience not as great as that of the udder with the shallow dent or division down the back of the udder, nor is the yield of milk as much. This may, of course, be an unjust generalization, but on the whole I favour a slight division.

A very marked cutting up between the quarters from the teats upwards is, however, not a good thing. The floor of the udder between the top of each teat should be straight and level.

HOW TO JUDGE A DAIRY COW

The photographs will illustrate better than my words, what I mean by a good udder.

Fleshy udders are condemned quite rightly by all judges of dairy cows. But we must distinguish between the fleshy and the muscular udder. An udder which milks out to leave a thin silky deeply folding udder hanging like an empty string or canvas shopping bag is not necessarily the best-wearing udder. I have known some exceptionally high yielding cows whose udders still looked half full after they had been milked out. This type of udder, though it does not fit the accepted measure of a perfect udder, will in my opinion, because of its muscular nature (surplus flesh or fat is another, and undesirable, matter) stand up to many lactations of hard wear without sagging or breaking down. I would not put too great a penalty on the udder which doesn't collapse completely after milking.

The next step in judging, after individual examinations, noting faults and perfections in the judging book together with any other comments likely to be useful in the final comparison, is to parade the animals around the ring once more. This further parade gives once more the general picture of each animal against the detailed close-up examination which has just been made. This 'standing back' view will help to confirm or deny first and second impressions and from this parade animals are drawn into the centre in the order in which they are, up to this stage in the judging, favoured. Two or three more animals than the number of prizes to be awarded are lined up across the middle of the ring, the animals not drawn in are asked to leave the ring. Comparative examinations are then made. The animals are handled and carefully compared on all points, and placed in strict order while their udders are still full; milking out follows and the final placing is done after a further examination of the udders when they are empty. Some breed societies still allow judging without milking out, but no man can place animals of any breed fairly without seeing their udders empty.

In the judging of maiden heifers the udder cannot play a very important part. Even more importance is placed then on bodies, legs, and general dairy character and appearance. Udders should nevertheless show signs of satisfactory development with the teats squarely and widely placed and with ample lose skin without surplus fat or flesh.

Bulls offer a problem in guesswork which most judges enjoy, though few regard as of any great importance in the evaluation of a bull. The only real means of assessment of a bull is his daughters and for this reason the classes for progeny groups, i.e. classes for three daughters of one bull, are the most valuable of all show classes anywhere. There is more satisfaction and more credit due, in the winning of a Progeny Group class than all the individual prizes in the show, and it is time show committees recognized this in their allocation of prize money. Exhibitors will not bring out their best groups in full force until more prize money is offered. It is an expensive business bringing out three animals, in addition (as sometimes is necessary) to the individual entries. So I feel that prize money in the progeny class should be at least three times the value of an individual prize. Then we may see some really good classes of progeny teams which will do more to improve our herds than all the classes for individual animals can ever do.

Chapter 7

PREPARING FOR SHOW
AND SHOWING OF CATTLE

Preparation for showing begins with the selection in the late autumn or winter of animals which are to be shown in the following summer. With animals which are to be shown freshly calved it will mean withholding the bull a little longer or allowing the cow to go to bull a little sooner than would otherwise have been the case, so that she will be looking at her best when she comes to show. The ideal stage at which to show a cow is about a month after calving. So it is important to be thinking at least ten months ahead of which cows or heifers to serve and when.

If you have studied and absorbed the chapter on judging, as well as the chapter on establishing and breeding the herd, then you will already have acquired an eye for the animal that is worth showing. You will, of course, have visited many shows and tried your skill at judging from the ringside as well as examining the prize-winning cows at close range in the cattle lines. That mind's-eye-model of your ideal dairy cow will have been measured against your best animals and one or two will have shown themselves to be worthy of a try out.

These animals, while they should not be fattened, should have at any rate the best of what's going in the way of food during the winter and if the winter is really cold it would be well to give them a rather milder time by shedding them, or at least yarding them on nights that they would normally be out. In this way they will not grow so much winter coat which will have to be taken off for the early shows. Further, steady building of condition gives even fleshing without surplus fat, whereas a short period of high feeding puts on fat unevenly.

About six weeks before the first show, preparation proper should start.

There are certain defects which would normally spoil an animal's chances in the ring and some which would debar her altogether. It is as well to look for these before making the final decision about which animals to show.

9. Good depth of barrel.

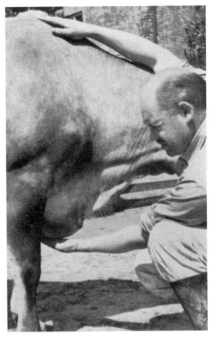

10. Depth and width of chest for good heart room.

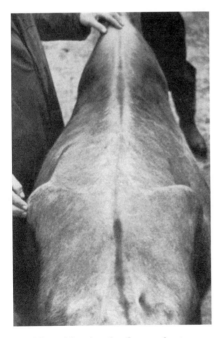

11. The wide triangle, fine neck at apex, broad base across hips.

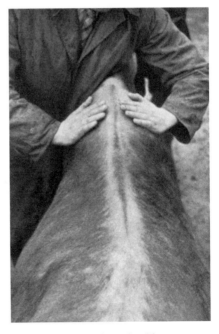

12. Fine sharp shoulders.

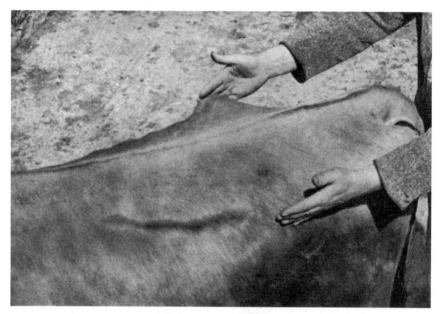

13. Width from hip to hip.

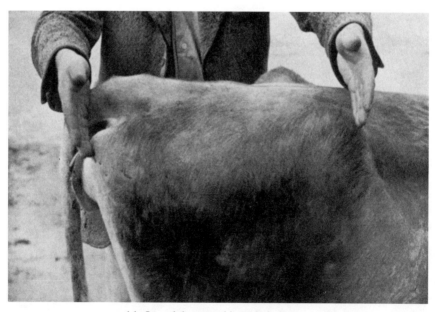

14. Length between hip and pin bones.

Lameness, even if it is only temporary, is generally an immediate disqualification with most judges. My own reaction to a lame entry is to investigate the reason and try to decide whether the defect is only very temporary. But don't count on other judges taking my way. I remember once I showed a Jersey cow in a class of over thirty entries. She had wrenched a hoof in being unloaded from the lorry and walked into the ring limping. The judge rejected her immediately, before she had passed round the ring once. But in an hour or two she was all right and went on to win the milking trials and in consequence was eligible for the Supreme Inspection Championship, open to all breeds. In this open championship she beat her own breed champion and the winner of the class from which earlier in the day she had been rejected and became reserve Supreme Champion.

But in most shows this second chance would not occur—so be sure that legs and feet are sound.

Enlarged knees result in some discrimination against an animal by the judge, but not in disqualification. If she is superior to the other entries in the normal breed characteristics and conformation she will still be highly placed, but it would take a brave judge to place a cow with a big knee in first place.

Udder. Blind quarters, or evidence of mastitis will cause immediate disqualification. An udder broken away from its attachment will almost certainly disqualify. A light or unbalanced quarter should be avoided, though except in a large class, it would not be greatly faulted, and if only very slightly uneven might even be levelled before entry to the ring.

Parrot jaw (overshot) or *Pig jaw* (undershot) would mean certain disqualification.

A twisted tail, though I wouldn't agree, especially if it is the result of an accident, is very much discriminated against by most judges.

Eyes. One blind eye would debar an animal from a prize, unless it was clear that the defect did not interfere with the normal life of the animal.

An over-fat yearling heifer would, in my judgment, be rejected at once. A fat heifer forward in calf might be excused if she was otherwise very dairylike, and showing signs of converting her surplus 'condition' into milk after calving. A fat cow would, unless she were close to calving and the type that seemed likely to milk it off, be marked down.

One further point to watch in selecting heifers and young bulls is the date of birth. There is always more chance of winning with a heifer or young bull born close to the limit of the class. An animal much younger than the oldest in a class for heifers or young bulls needs to be of really outstanding merit to compete. For the nearer to maturity an animal has reached, the less the judge has to estimate its probable developments.

Each animal should be thoroughly brushed to get all loose hairs, mud and dust from the coat. Then they should be washed all over with warm water and a liquid shampoo. Then a cover of some kind, its thickness depending on the coldness of the weather, should be put on each animal. This may, for the period before the show, be made up of sacking, but it should cover the animal completely from the base of the neck to the tail setting and down to the floor of the belly. The rug should be tied under the girth (or right around if possible), around the chest and behind the udder—another tie just in front of the udder would also help.

I hope this advice to use a rug so long before the show may soon be out of date. At present it is almost impossible to compete in the show ring without having rugged your entry in order to get the skin as thin and the coat as sleek and fine as possible. The day may come, and the sooner the better for you and me who have no time for elaborate show preparations, when judges will judge the cow and not the amount of superficial preparation which has been made on her before the show. But until then, we must if we are to hope to win or even be placed, go through most of these preparations.

From this stage until the show—the most important job is daily grooming—apart of course from the need for maintaining the animal in good condition.

For this you will need a steel comb for the tail, a stiff dandy brush and a softer short-bristled brush, and a section of thick rubber lorry tyre. A curry comb may also be needed occasionally for scraping off dung which may get caked on the hocks or pin bones with some animals. But daily attention should avoid the need for this.

Each day give a brisk brush over with the dandy brush then follow with the piece of rubber tyre. Be careful on a thin-skinned animal not to raise weals with a too vigorous use of the dandy brush. The edge of the rubber tyre should be used to scrape off loose hairs. This is far more effective than any kind of brush as the rubber edge of the tyre grips the hairs which, under the warming effect of the rug the animal now wears continuously, have started to fall. What in effect you have done with the rug is to speed the arrival of spring or early summer by raising the surface temperature by friction of the rug, and the retention of body heat, and caused the animal to shed his or her winter growth of hair when *you* decide instead of waiting for the weather. Good feeding, by raising the energy or warmth generated in the body, also contributes to this process.

By a fortnight or ten days before the show most of the winter coat should have fallen and a new growth of bright fine and silky hair will have followed it. Frequent use of the dandy and soft brush will have split the hair as it grew and produced a finer denser coat.

Useful tips for the encouragement of a bright, rich-coloured coat of dense fine hair are as follows:

The diet should include a small proportion—say 10 percent of linseed meal or cake. A bran mash made with diluted molasses every other day for a fortnight before the show will also add lustre to the hair. But finest of all supplements for dense and colourful coat is seaweed powder, meal or cubes. The meal and cubes are available ready for use as a food to be used in quantities up to 10 percent of the ration. The finer seaweed powder has all the natural trace elements and minerals, medicinal and health corrective properties, as well as encouraging the right condition in the coat, and is given in the other dry food at the rate of a teaspoonful daily for yearlings or a dessertspoonful daily for mature cows. Available from herbal firms.

Training. Any animal which is not accustomed to being led on a halter will need to be trained many weeks before the show. Nothing penalizes an animal more than the inability of its herdsman to walk it gracefully around the ring and to move it and pose it in such a way as to show it at its best—or even to conceal, by judicious manoeuvring, one or more minor but otherwise noticeable faults. I have seen bulls in the ring which have been quite unapproachable, and no judge has the patience to dance round a bull swivelling on its front feet, in an attempt to handle him. Such bulls will not be judged, and for the want of a few hours' training you may miss the supreme award.

The ideal time to accustom a heifer to handling is before it goes out to grazing as a yearling or bulling heifer. A bull, though manageable when he is rung at ten months old, should also be handled before reaching that age. At some stage during the first twelve months of life the animal should be haltered and tied for a week or two. If calves or heifers are out by day and brought indoors at nights it is a good plan to arrange for ties at which they may have their food. They will then associate tying and human control with the pleasure of eating, and when the time comes to train them to be led they will co-operate willingly.

Lead them for a short time each day, five minutes to start with and increase the period daily until the animal walks gracefully and with an alert and springy gait.

The objecting animal will probably stand quite firm at first and refuse to move forward. Don't tie it to the back of the tractor and draw it forward by force! Turn to one side or the other, and go round in circles if the animal prefers it that way. Alternatively move to the back of the animal and gently urge her forward from the rear, giving her a certain amount of head. But be sure in this case that you can retain a hold on the animal, or she may chase away, dragging you headlong behind. First journeys should be made for a definite purpose which is pleasurable to the animal—i.e. to food or water. Whatever you do avoid force, the use of a stick or a dog, or one of the modern electrically charged 'goads'.

Two people will be needed for the early training—one to lead and the other to encourage on from behind. Quietness and gentleness are absolutely essential. Shouting and hitting will only prolong the agony.

Once reasonable forward movement has been achieved, the animal should be taught to move with slow, even strides; to stop slowly and to pose with feet evenly and squarely placed. A gentle but not too obvious pull forward or push backward on the halter (gripped closely to the head with the right hand, loose end rolled up in or around the left hand) should be sufficient to correct the standing position. A touch with your foot on the foot of the cow—just above her hoof in front—or just under the dew claws behind, will cause a wrongly placed leg to be moved in the direction you desire.

Lead the animal from her left side, close up to her head (though you may step away once she is moving well and provided her head is upright and alert in order to show her off alone). But she must be trained to be led from either side in case the judge asks you to parade in the opposite direction. For it is wise never to stand between the judge and your animal, unless you have something to hide.

The proper stance, for a correct animal, is with both front and hind feet squarely placed and slightly stretched to exaggerate length, yet a comfortable distance apart. A slight slackness in the loins or weakness in the back may be corrected by standing the front and hind feet rather closer together—or at least front and back legs on one side nearer to one another so that the middle of the back is raised a little. Momentarily, this may be achieved by giving the animal a gentle push back on to her hind legs just before the judge looks at her—though a definite weakness in the loin cannot long be concealed from an experienced judge.

If the animal has tendency to stand with a sloping rump or an arching back provided it is not a marked physical defect, a nip with the fingers on the back will cause her to dip into normal position.

While training the animal to lead and eventually to show him or herself to good advantage, be careful not to slip into the most undesirable habit which some herdsmen or cattle handlers acquire in the ring. Avoid waving your hands about and attracting attention to your animal. If it is worth a prize the judge won't miss the fact. Learn to show the animal to the best of its advantage, but to show in such a way as to persuade the judge that you aren't there. In other words that nothing you have done has altered in any way the natural yet superior ability of your animal to win on its own showing.

A week before the show another shampoo is advisable. With the Jersey this should not be left nearer than four or five days before the show because of the much thinner skin and finer hair needing more time to recover its natural appearance, but all other breeds may be washed at any time up to the morning of the show and even on the morning of the show.

Work should now commence on the correction of minor faults in the horns, feet, and general appearance of the animal. This can be done by trimming and filing the horns, trimming the feet (though where there was excessive growth of the hoof this should have been corrected immediately it was seen) and clipping the hair in certain places.

Horn-trimming should have started as a yearling. If there is any indication that the shape of the horns is likely to be unattractive they can easily be encouraged to grow in the desired direction as soon as the direction of the natural growth is evident. This can be done by boring a hole—with a brace and bit—and threading a wire from one horn-tip to the other. A piece of lead piping may be used (flattened with a hammer before threading the wire through the horns so that the wire passing through it is fixed) over the forehead to tighten the wire periodically in the manner of a tourniquet.

If the horns are growing too cocked, they may be brought down by increasing the weight of lead piping. Filing the horns with a three-cornered file to make two or three nicks nearly to the quick of the horn will encourage the growth in the direction of the side on which the nicks are made. If the horns are sharply pointed the tips may be taken off and rounded.

With an older animal which has not had its horns trained, much may still be done to bring them into a more attractive shape. Filing down on the inside of the middle of the horn and outside of the end of the horn will help to shape it in. Removal of the end if it is badly shaped on one side will help to even the balance of the horns. If the animal is not more than two years old it will still be possible to improve the shape by wiring the horns for a few months.

A week or so before the show is too late to effect changes in the direction of growth and all that can be done is to make the best of the horns as they are by means of a coarse rasp and a finer file.

PREPARING FOR SHOW AND SHOWING CATTLE

The day before the show, or even on the morning of the show, horns should be scraped with a piece of broken glass to remove all the scratches and dirt. They are best finished off with No. 2 emery paper. Just before the animal goes into the ring, paint the horns with clear varnish or linseed oil to give the final gloss. Varnish will last glossy all day but watch that it doesn't gather bits of hay and dust before it is dry. Oil will need repainting just before each entry to the ring.

Clipping should not be done all over. Occasionally one sees an animal in the show ring which has been clipped all over and it is so difficult to conceal the fact that most judges are inclined to be rather prejudiced against it. It is far better to start preparation early and get the winter hair off with rugging, grooming and the piece of rubber tyre.

All that should be done with the clipper is to give the finishing touches which make the animal so much more correct, of clean-cut lines and alert. With the Ayrshire this means clipping all the hairs from the head and neck back to the shoulders plus the tail and udder, and where necessary top-line trimming. Some Ayrshire breeders run the machine right down the back bone to a width of about four inches all the way. Less frequently I have seen this done with other breeds but on the whole I don't consider it an improvement.

The important trimmings which apply to all breeds are to clip the hair as short as possible on the tail from just above the switch to the tail setting. Around the tail setting and along the top line at least to the hips, the clippers should be used to produce clean and level appearance, especially in profile. Bumps may be levelled by taking off the hair on top and leaving it there in the dips or hollows, but it must be done very carefully so that the unclipped part merges into the clipped part without looking too obvious.

Whether or not, with breeds other than the Ayrshire, the hair on the head should be clipped depends on the neatness or otherwise of the animal's appearance without such clipping. Very often the animal has a rough and tufty growth of hair between the horns and around and in the ears, and considerable improvement in smartness can be achieved by clipping it. It is rarely wise, however, to clip the hair of the face other than the forehead.

Bulls of all breeds, as well as the Ayrshire, grow long and sometimes coarse hair along the crest and this should be removed to show off and strengthen the masculinity of the head and neck.

In short, the object of clipping is to emphasize the good points and if possible, legitimately to camouflage the bad.

The udder of a milking animal should, of course, be clipped all over if this has not already been done for normal milking efficiency and cleanliness.

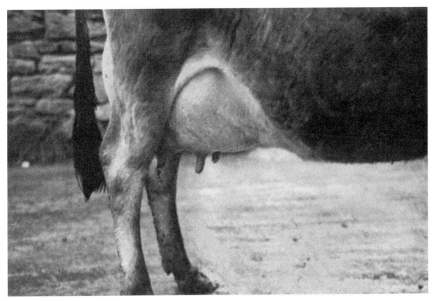

15. A well-shaped, well-attached udder, between strong straight legs.

16. A badly attached udder, and weak hind legs with sickle hocks.

17. A cow (Polden Dolly Daydream) before preparation for show.

18. The same cow prepared for show.

At home, this trimming is best done with a mechanical clipper driven from the vacuum line of the milking machine or by electricity. But it is well to have a set of hand clippers to give the final touches at the show.

The tail switch is greatly improved by a thorough washing and, with a little soap lather finally left in the hair, plait it in six or eight plaits, with a tape of cloth or muslin to each two locks of hair. All the plaits will be swathed in sacking so that no dung or urine can penetrate to the hair and soil or wet it before the show. This is done a day or so before the show—at latest the night before—though the longer the better, up to four or five days before the show. When these plaits are untied and taken down an hour or so before the animal enters the ring and the switch combed out—outwards from the bone of the tail, an attractive crimped appearance is achieved. This gives the last touch of quality and grandeur to the beast, which while quite unimportant in relation to the major attributes of a good bull or cow, does give that finished picture which is so pleasing to exhibitor and judge alike, and other things being equal, may even, whether he admits it or not, give that little stroke of appeal to the judge which helps to sway the decision.

For the man who is to handle the animal in the ring there are two or three important points.

Always have a spotlessly clean white coat for the first appearance in the ring. If this gets a little shabby during the course of the day for the later classes that can't be helped.

See that boots are clean and that whatever clothes are evident beneath the white coat, are tidy.

Never smoke in the ring and never lounge about or lean on the animal while waiting for the judge to get around to his close up inspection. Always be on the alert and always keep one eye on the judge ready to be called in or—and be sporting about it if you are— turned out. 'Show' your exhibit continuously for the judge will often look back to compare a point when you may not expect it.

When the judging is finished there will be a chance to learn why your animal has been placed where it was. Most judges will gladly go along the lines afterwards and answer questions about the animals and the judging of them. At some shows recently, the judge has been asked to give a short talk in the ring explaining his placings. This is asking rather a lot of the judge, but where he is willing and the time allows, it produces most profitable guidance to exhibitors for future showing.

Section Three

MANAGEMENT FOR MILK PRODUCTION

Chapter 8

PREPARING THE HEIFER
AND COW FOR LACTATION

Tremendous publicity has been given to 'steaming up' or feeding high-protein milk-stimulating foods which often have the effect, and indeed are advocated for the very purpose, of bringing a heifer to her milk before she calves. This practice, known as steaming up and pre-milking, presents the intelligent herdsman with a very big and puzzling problem. For no thoughtful person can consider such a practice as in any way likely to benefit the heifer.

Many dairy farmers have nevertheless been attracted by the prospect of one or two hundred more gallons of milk (the increased yield claimed by its originators for the system of steaming up and pre-milking) and have done everything possible to encourage by feeding, udder massage, and even by hormone injections (though this is not officially advocated) to get heifers to milk before calving.

I suppose orthodox dairy farming has been developed so far along unnatural lines that I shall be considered merely reactionary and pig-headed if I condemn this practice on grounds of its unnaturalness. The whole process of milk production, as indeed farming of any kind, is patently unnatural. But unless it is artificial insemination, which is no doubt still the supreme abomination of man's relationship with animals, there is no practice which I would condemn more. For whereas practically all other farming operations, except the use of chemicals and poison sprays, are in line with nature or in co-operation with nature and at worst a mere deviation of a natural process, the stimulation of milk secretion before the act of parturition, is a direct reversal of a natural process. In nature a mammal, whether cow, elephant or the farmer's wife, produces milk after, and more important *because of*, the act of giving birth. To cause the milk to flow before the calf is born is to put nature into reverse with consequences which, like those which may follow artificial insemination, cannot be estimated in advance.

19. Winter coat as it begins to shed in the spring. Polden Dreaming Dorothy.

20. Rubbing off the winter hair—see plate 22 for finished effect.

21. Polishing the horns with emery paper.

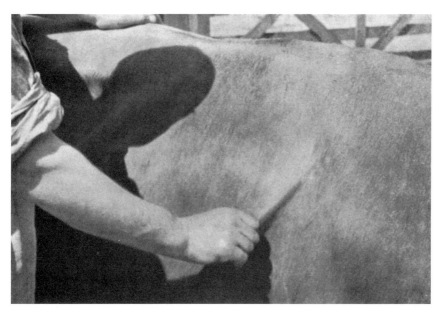

22. A fine loose skin, showing the finished effect after removing winter hair.

PREPARING THE HEIFER AND COW FOR LACTATION

Some of the consequences of steaming-up and pre-milking have never-theless already shown themselves, to the everlasting sorrow of the farmers who were gullible enough or mercenary enough to try the system. Would that the physical suffering involved had been the lot of the originators of the system and not the animals! But I have seen and heard of many heifers which have been steamed-up, pre-milked and admittedly produced phe-nomenal yields of milk during the early weeks of the lactation following calving, but which have had serious mastitis and might as well have been allowed a normal calving and a normal yield and come through to the end with healthy udders for all the ultimate gain has proved to be.

One large herd of pedigree Jerseys, which I advised, is typical of many such examples of rushing into this system which the loud trumpets of enthu-siasm proclaimed before it had been proved by the measured results of time and wisdom. The owner wrote saying that because the advice to steam-up and pre-milk had come from semi-official sources—a well-known agricul-tural college and some district advisers of the National Agricultural Advisory Service, he assumed that the method was scientifically sound and well proven by long testing to be harmless, and he adopted it in his herd without further investigation. After all, he said, our colleges and ministry scientists exist to do the investigation and pass to the farmer that information and guidance which is proved to be foolproof and profitable to the farmer, and to keep reasonably quiet about new theories especially unnatural ones, which are still the subject of experiment. Admittedly he got the big yields—some Jersey heifers yielding 2 gallons of milk a day before calving and going up to 6 gallons on calving—but every one of them went down with mastitis or acetonaemia or both before the lactation had progressed very far. When I was called in he had a shed half full of formerly highly valuable heifers all wrong in one or more quarters. These heifers had started off yielding heav-ily but had given a total lactation yield far less than would have been given had they been fed normally and allowed to come to their milk at the time of, instead of some weeks before, calving. Fortunately we cured most of them by the mastitis treatment I have described on page 122, and prevented further trouble by following the methods of management advocated in this book and my book, *Fertility Farming*. But that farmer, along with many who did likewise, cursed the day he ever heard of those unproven theories.

Fortunately, though it has received no publicity of the kind that was accorded the harmful theories of steaming-up and pre-milking the origina-tors of this practice appear to have modified it somewhat and now I believe advocate milking a heifer before she calves only to relieve her, instead of advising the *actual encouragement* of milk secretion before calving. This

74

of course is sheer common sense. If, on the rare occasions that a heifer is seen to be uncomfortable as a result of coming to her milk before calving, then it is obvious that she must be relieved. But only when, through circumstances beyond human control, the milk comes before the calf, should it be drawn other than at the normal after-calving stage. To milk a heifer deliberately and regularly, and to give her food which stimulates milk secretion, for the sole purpose of extracting milk prematurely, as was until recently urged by some authorities, can bring only disaster to our cattle and consequently lead the owners of these cattle into difficulties from which neither the Minister of Agriculture nor his officials will have the inclination, let alone the ability, to extricate them.

But the fact that I deplore steaming-up (which really means *over*-feeding with *over*-stimulating concentrates) and pre-milking, does not mean that I would not have my heifers in really good condition at the time of calving, nor that I would leave a heifer which prematurely secretes her milk, unrelieved (as I have already explained). Heifers can, however, be brought to first class calving and milking condition on herbal leys in summer and silage in winter, without any concentrates whatever. And the ultimate health and economical milk production of the future cow, in my experience, demands entirely natural and mainly bulky low-protein food up to the time of second calving. Animals so fed are far more likely to put up good life-time yields—and cost their owners nothing in veterinary bills—than those fed on concentrates during heifer-hood (i.e. the in-calf and milking heifer period of their lives).

The feeding of a dry cow does involve a rather higher level of nutrition for she will have lost a good deal of flesh during the completed lactation. But again, I am convinced that overfeeding with high-protein foods, including leys close to the time of calving, is a primary cause of milk fever and acetonaemia (see pages 123 and 110, respectively). So that while I bring the dry cow to a good condition by about the third week before calving, all concentrates, even home-grown cereals, are cut out for at least the two weeks immediately before calving. If the cow is on lush pasture or ley, this, too, is severely rationed. A complete fast is given on the day before, the day of, and the day after calving, giving during that time water only. This, together with the adequate supply of herbs in the grazing and the addition, if possible, of seaweed as manure via the soil, or as powder or meal via the mouth, is a sure safeguard against milk fever.

Perhaps the greatest mistake of all in cow feeding is to give large quantities of high protein food a week or two before and after calving, in the hope that more milk will be produced. This is a firm invitation for the cow to get indigestion at best, and at worst acetonaemia or milk fever.

The time to prepare for the next lactation in improving the condition of the cow, is three months before she calves—in drying her off for at least two months' rest, and feeding her reasonably well over the whole period of the rest—except the last two weeks before calving. Neglect to maintain the cow's condition during her dry period cannot be made up three weeks or so before she calves again.

Drying-Off a Cow in Milk

All kinds of involved methods of drying off a cow in milk have been written about, talked about and tried, from sterilizing the udder and teats, injecting penicillin into each quarter and sealing up with collodian, to merely shirking it altogether and milking the cow right through without rest. But the obvious way to stop a cow giving milk is to stop milking her and quite simply that is how I dry a cow off. If a cow is not milked she will stop making milk. Milk production continues in nature only as a result of the continuing stimulation of the suckling young. If suckling ceases milk secretion ceases without harm to the cow. Similarly assuming the udder is healthy as it will be in an organically fed herd, no harm will come to the cow, however much milk she is giving, if milking stops quite abruptly without any gradual reduction in the frequency of milking. And, once you accept my now oft demonstrated theory that mastitis arises inherently and not primarily as a result of external bacterial infection, you will realize the utter futility of disinfecting the udder, injecting penicillin, or sealing each quarter with collodian.

Of course, if the cow is giving much more than say three gallons of milk a day, it is probably more convenient and economical to let her milk through continuously and serve her rather later during the next lactation to allow a longer rest—three to four months—before a subsequent calf.

There is no need to be foolhardy in risking udder trouble, especially if the cow has not got a generation or two of 'fertility farming' in her ancestry as well as her own life. So, two days after milking has been stopped, and again at intervals of two or three days for a week or ten days, examine her udder, draw a few drops of milk from each quarter and make sure that there is no inflammation. On the second day and for the first week or so after stopping milking, the udder may appear to be slightly distended. But it is unlikely to reach the point of discomfort to the cow at this stage of the lactation. Once the udder is completely filled, little or no more milk will be produced by the system.

It is well to withhold completely all food for forty-eight hours, if convenient, before milking is stopped. This will speed the cessation of milk secretion and at the same time benefit the general health of the cow. Let her have limited water during this fast—three or four gallons a day.

Chapter 9

FEEDING AND CROPPING
FOR THE DAIRY HERD

In estimating the feeding requirements of the dairy herd calculate to provide basic maintenance entirely from grass, either as silage and grazing—hay and grazing—or best of all silage, hay and grazing.

Then provide milk production requirements from a combination of grass and arable, i.e. first quality grazing in the summer with first quality silage from grass leys and arable crops such as oats, dredge corn, beans or linseed, in the winter.

Winter and summer maintenance requirements, though varying considerably from one cow to another—even within a breed,—may be calculated from the following rough guide. But using this as a guide only, allow more, or less per head for the period, according to the general condition of the animal.

Breed	Total requirements per cow			
	Winter 6 months		Summer 6 months plus daily average of 2 gallons of milk	
	Best ley hay	Old pasture or simple mixture ley hay	New herbal ley	Simple mixture or poor ley
	cwt.	cwt.	acres	acres
Jerseys, Dexters	20	30	$\frac{1}{2}-\frac{3}{4}$	$1-1\frac{1}{4}$
Kerry, Ayrshire, Guernseys	30	45	$\frac{3}{4}-1$	$1\frac{1}{4}-1\frac{1}{2}$
Shorthorns, Friesians	40	55	$1\frac{1}{4}$	2
Devons, Red Polls	45	60	$1\frac{1}{2}$	$2\frac{1}{2}$

From a knowledge of yields on your farm the acreage required for hay may then be calculated.

For individual cows a good way of arriving at the required maintenance ration is to take the live weight in hundredweights, subtract one and multiply by two. This gives the maint enance requirements in pounds of hay. For instance, a Jersey cow weighing 7 cwt. will require $7 - 1 = 6 \times 2$ is 12 lb. hay each day to keep her fit and active, but not producing.

A maintenance ration may then be devised by using the following table of hay equivalents:

> 3 lb. silage = 1 lb. of hay
> 4 lb. kale equals 1 lb. of hay
> 1 lb. oat straw (unthreshed) equals 1 lb. hay
> 1 lb. oat straw (threshed) equals 1 lb. hay
> 1 lb. straw plus 3 lb. roots equals 1 lb. hay
> $\frac{2}{3}$ lb. dried beet pulp equals 1 lb. hay
> 1 lb. undried beet pulp equals 1 lb. hay

If homegrown cereals are being fed for production, then silage may be fed *ad lib.* for maintenance, or in conjunction with other roughage such as good oat straw, kale, mangolds, or hay.

Where silage, kale, or cabbage, or a combination of these with hay is to be used, I take the following as my guide:

Winter

Period of approximately 170 days.
1 lb. a day a head = approximately $1\frac{1}{2}$ cwt.

KALE

Allow an average of:

> 30 lb. daily for cows: 45 cwt.
> 10 lb. daily for young stock: 15 cwt.

On an estimated yield of 15 tons an acre this means that a herd of equal numbers of cows and young stock would need one-fifth acre a cow.

SILAGE

Allow the same quantities as kale, that is 3 tons per cow to cover cattle of all ages where young stock and cows are in equal numbers.

On an arable silage crop of say oats and vetches this can be grown on one-third acre so that a herd of 30 cows and 30 followers would need ten acres of oats and vetches or similar silage crop.

HAY

If hay is to form the bulk of your maintenance ration allow 15 lb. a cow, and 8 lb. a head young stock, or just over 1 ton per cow and 12 cwt. each for young stock.

If the allowance of kale and silage are as above and you have oat straw for bulky dry fodder, then hay may be dispensed with altogether, or at most fed to the youngest stock only, when an average allowance of 5 to 8 lb. a head with some kale or silage will be enough for cattle up to eighteen months old.

Summer and Winter Grazing Requirements

On first-class leys including the deep-rooting herbs on strong fertile land, one acre should feed one cow and one head of young stock throughout the summer.

On poorer land and less productive leys allow $1\frac{1}{4}$ acres per cow and $\frac{3}{4}$ acre per head of young stock. An additional 1 acre per head of young stock and dry cows will be needed for winter grazing, supplemented by oat straw and/or kale or silage, and winter weed grazing.

To summarize, the requirements of a dairy herd on a *per cow* basis assuming equal numbers of young stock, are:

	Acre per cow
Kale	$\frac{1}{5}$
Arable, silage crop	$\frac{1}{3}$
Hay (permanent grass)	1
Hay (seeds ley)	$\frac{1}{2}$
Oats	1
Linseed or Beans	$\frac{1}{2}$
Grazing (good)	1
Grazing (poor)	2
Winter grazing	1

Production Rations

Cereals. Allow 3 lb. per gallon of milk, or 1 ton (approx.) for a 700-gallon cow, which on average yields is 1 acre of oats per cow.

Protein food. 1 lb. per gallon of milk which for 700-gallons may be obtained from half-acre per cow of linseed or beans or peas.

As grass will supply the production requirements of a large part of the milk yield the above production allowances will also cover the requirements of young stock in the limited instances where meal feeding is given.

The best possible production ration from the point of view of health of the cattle, which a good farmer always considers before excessive-yield producing rations, is the simple mixture of ground oats and linseed or beans in the following ratio:

> 3 lb. ground oats,
> 1 lb. ground linseed or beans,

both ground at frequent intervals so that the full freshness of the oil of the linseed and the oat, as well as essential vitamins shall be retained. Though not always possible, daily grinding is the ideal.

Examples of Complete Rations for Maintenance and Production

For a Jersey cow giving 1 gallon of milk:

(a)	Hay (average quality)	15 lb.
	Molassed silage	15 lb.
(b)	Hay (average quality)	15 lb.
	Kale	20 lb.
(c)	Hay (average quality)	15 lb.
	Crushed oats	4 lb.

For a Jersey cow giving 2 gallons of milk:

(a)	Hay (average quality)	10 lb.
	Molassed silage	30 lb.
(b)	Hay (average quality)	15 lb.
	Mangolds	50 lb.
	Bean meal	2 lb.

For a Jersey cow giving 3 gallons of milk:

(a)	Hay (first quality)	15 lb.
	Molassed silage (first quality)	30 lb.
	or	
	Ground oats	9 lb.
	Ground linseed or beans	3 lb.
(b)	Hay (average quality)	10 lb.
	Mangolds	25 lb.
	Bean meal or linseed meal	3 lb.
	Crushed cereals (oats)	12 lb.

The wisest course from a health standpoint is to allow natural foods, *ad lib.*, as available, rationing carefully only the more stimulating concentrated foods.

As a rich source of all the minerals and trace elements found in nature, and essential to the general health and especially the fecundity of the cow, seaweed in some form should be fed as a supplement. A teaspoonful daily of the best quality seaweeds blended in powder form or 10 percent of the straight seaweed food. Alternatively or additionally—though this has a long-term effect—apply seaweed raw, or via the compost heap or as a powdered fertilizer, to the soil in which the food of the cattle is grown.

Feeding Routine

If a production ration has been worked out, it is fed at the rate of $3\frac{1}{2}$ or 4 lb. per gallon of milk being given by the cow over and above what may be expected from the maintenance ration. The orthodox system of arriving at a production ration on the basis of protein and starch equivalents, while providing a useful rough guide must not be relied upon to give entirely satisfactory results. A far better measure of the needs of a cow are the herdsman's own eyes and the application of his intelligence and instinct. This means that feeding should be adjusted to the individual requirements of each cow, as shown by her day-to-day performance and appearance.

Whatever the ration or the quantity, the best routine to follow in order to ensure optimum output from the cow is to keep the quantity of production ration approximately a gallon ahead of the cow each week from the second week after calving, until she shows no further sign of increased yield. Then gradually lower the ration till she is getting the exact requirements per gallon of her yield. This peak period will last for some weeks before the fall in yield gives the sign for a further change in ration. But don't drop the production ration immediately there is a drop in yield. The fall in milk yield may be due to some other factor than food or the advancing stage of the lactation. Wait till the end of a week, then continue another week feeding a ration for half a gallon more than the average yield for the week of the fall in yield. If, after this week, there is no return to a higher yield then it may be assumed that the lowering yield is normal and feeding should be adjusted accordingly. But always keep the lower production ration a week behind the lower yield.

The production ration for each week may be determined by taking the average daily yield at the end of the week and feeding for the coming week at that daily rate per gallon.

Bull Feeding

Mature bulls, indeed all weaned bulls, are best limited entirely to grass in the summer and silage, hay, oat straw and kale or roots in the winter. If these foods are available in quantities to satisfy his appetite the working bull is better without any kind of concentrate feeding. One of my best show bulls has never touched anything but grass and other bulky foods since he was a year old and he is still working at 11 years old and likely to continue for some years yet. What is more he always reaches high condition for the summer shows if tethered on grass as soon as there is any.

Cropping for the Dairy Herd

As a basis for calculating the cropping requirements of the dairy herd I have worked out a table which gives all the information that is likely to be required. From the size of the herd and the information given in the section on 'Feeding the Herd' the required quantity of any crop may be estimated. It is an easy matter, then, from the following table to work out the acreage needed—seed required to sow that acreage and the time to sow that acreage. But to allow for bad weather during growing or harvesting allow about 25 percent bigger acreage as a safety margin. For instance, if you are sowing oats for thirty cows you will need 1 ton a cow. A yield of 25 cwt. per acre may be expected so you should allow thirty acres. The seed for this will be approximately 120 bushels if it is to be drilled or 180 bushels broadcast, and times of sowing are August to October or February and March.

The basic preventative of all animal diseases and the finest source of summer and winter feeding (as grazing and silage or hay) is the organically grown herbal ley. The following is a mixture which provides a wide variety of the essentials of health and abundant production, which is suitable for all classes of soil.

THE GOOSEGREEN HERBAL LEY MIXTURE
in lb. per acre

3 lb. Perennial Ryegrass (S.23)
3 lb. Perennial Ryegrass (S.24)
3 lb. Cocksfoot (S.143) } on light or medium land
3 lb. Cocksfoot (S.26)
Plus/or 3 lb. Timothy (S.51) } on heavy land
3 lb. Timothy (S.48)
1 lb. Rough Stalked Meadow Grass

1 lb. Tall Fescue
1 lb. Late Flowering Red Clover (Montgomery or Aberystwyth)
1 lb. White Clover (S.100)
1 lb. Wild White Clover
1 lb. Alsike
2 lb. Chicory
3 lb. Burnet
¼ lb. Yarrow
2 lb. Sheep's Parsley
2 lb. American Sweet Clover
1 lb. Kidney Vetch
2 lb. Lucerne
1 lb. Broad Leaved Plantain, or Ribgrass
Plus 6 lb. Italian Ryegrass if sown direct

Omit yarrow if indigenous.

For detailed information regarding cultivations by fertility farming methods read my book, *Fertility Farming.*

As a means of providing quickly the most valuable herbs in fields where simple mixtures are already sown, and not to be broken for a year or two, I have devised the following Hedgerow Herbal Mixture which may be sown at any time from the end of March to mid-September around the hedgerows, on the disced headland or on the banks. Close to the hedge where the soil is loose and friable from leaf-fall, it is enough merely to sprinkle the seed in the loose soil. Otherwise rake the seed in to ensure quick germination.

Even where a herbal ley occupies the whole field, additional health assurance for the herd may be gained by sowing the hedgerow mixture.

Additionally, plant hazel and raspberry. Hazel leaves benefit the colour and quality of milk; raspberry is a tonic for the reproductive system of the cow and the bull.

HEDGEROW HERBAL MIXTURE FOR COWS, GOATS AND HORSES

1 lb. Comfrey
1 lb. Chicory
1 lb. Sheep's Parsley
1 lb. Burnt
1 lb. Ribgrass (Plantain)
1 lb. Sweet Clover
1 lb. Kidney Vetch
1 lb. Caraway
$\frac{1}{4}$ lb. Yarrow

$8\frac{1}{4}$ lb. an acre
An approximate cost of 30/- an acre.

Bushel weights and seeding rates assuming normal purity and germination
Yields assuming average fertility and organic methods

Seed	Weight per bushel	How sown	Seed required per acre	Time of Sowing (inclusive)	Acreage yields to expect
	lb.		*bush.*		
Barley	50–56		2–4	Dec.–May	25 cwt.
Maize	60		$1\frac{1}{4}$–$2\frac{1}{4}$	Mar.–May	20 tons (green)
Oats	38–45	{ Drilled { Broadcast	3–$5\frac{1}{2}$ $4\frac{1}{2}$–7	Aug.–Oct. } Feb.–Mar. }	25 cwt.
Rye for corn		56–60	2–3	Autumn	20–30 cwt.
Rye for green fodder	—		3–4	Any time	10 tons
Wheat	60–63	{ Drilled { Broadcast	$1\frac{1}{2}$–3 3–4	Aug.–Oct. Feb.–Mar.	25–40 cwt. 20–30 cwt.
Beans		62–66	2–4	Sept.–Oct.	$\frac{1}{4}$ to 1 ton
Peas		62–64	2–3	Dec.–Mar.	20–30 cwt.
Buckwheat	50	{ Drilled { Broadcast	1–2 2–$2\frac{1}{2}$	} Mar.–May	1 ton
			lb.		
Cabbage	50–56	{ Drilled { Transplant	4–6 2–$2\frac{1}{2}$	Aug. & Feb. } Oct. & Mar. }	20 tons
Carrot	30	Drilled	8–10	Feb.–June	15 tons
Kale	50–56	{ Drilled { Broadcast	4–6 10	} Feb.–July	20 tons
Kohl Rabi	50–56	Drilled	3–5	Feb.–April	15 tons
Lucerne (Alfalfa)	62–64	D. or B.	20–28	Aug. or April	{ 20 tons 30 tons green
Mangold	16–20	Drilled	7–8	Mar.–April	30–40 tons
Mustard, white	50–56	Broadcast	20	Any time	Green manure
Parsnip		17–19	6–8	Spring	12–15 tons
			cwt.		
Potato		56	12–20	Spring	10–15 tons
			lb.		
Rape	50–56	{ Drilled { Broadcast	4–6 10–16	} Feb.–Aug.	12–15 tons
Sainfoin, milled	62	Drilled	56	} Spring or August	3 tons per acre, green
Sainfoin, in husk	20–28	Drilled	*bush.* 4		
			lb.		
Sugar Beet	16–20	Drilled	12	April	12–20 tons
Swede	50–56	Drilled	3–4	Feb.–July	15–20 tons
Turnip	50–52	Drilled	2–4	Feb.–July	12–15 tons
			bush.		
Vetches or Tare, and Oats or Rye	60–64	Drilled	1 plus 2 oats *or* Rye	Spring or Autumn	10 tons green
			lb.		
Flax, for linseed	52–56	D. or B.	40–60	April	10–20 cwt.
Herbal ley mixture	—	D. or B.	38–46	April or Sept.	2 tons hay 4–6 tons silage

Chapter 10

CALF REARING

I f the future health of a calf is to be assured, natural rearing on a foster
mother is imperative. A cow giving 6–8 lb. milk a day is sufficient for
calves of all breeds and is the best means of rearing a calf well, both
for the health and growth of the calf and the most economical use of milk.
Nearly double the quantity is required to give similar results from bucket
feeding; but failing a nurse cow and only in such an emergency would I
permit it, feed as follows from a bucket:

Milk fresh from the cow per day		Dry Food	Hay and/or Silage (Good quality)	Water
week	quarts			
1st	4	—	—	—
2nd	4	—	—	—
3rd	4	—	—	—
4th	4	Offered	—	—
5th	$3\frac{1}{2}$	Then give	Offered	Offered
6th	3	from 1 lb. to	Ad lib.	Ad lib.
7th	3	$1\frac{1}{2}$ lb.	Ad lib.	Ad lib.
8th	3	daily as	Ad lib.	Ad lib.
9th	2	cleaned up	Ad lib.	Ad lib.
10th–12th	$1\frac{1}{2}$	made up to	Ad lib.	Ad lib.
12th–14th	1	1 gallon with	Ad lib.	Ad lib.
14th–20th	1 pint	water if possible	Ad lib.	Ad lib.

Milk fed in three meals daily.

The best meal ration for calves is home-grown oats 3 parts and linseed
2 parts, both ground to a meal, mixed and fed dry with the addition of a
little coarsely ground wheat, fed at the rate of 2 percent of liveweight.
But where good silage and/or hay is available *ab lib.*, these form the
perfect food for calves from weaning stage, and as a supplement to

86

suckling. I avoid any kind of meal or cake until the animal calves her second calf. The feeding of unnatural concentrates in early life is the surest way of impairing digestion and ensuring disease in cowhood.

The main aim in calf rearing and feeding for dairy purposes should be big bellies, bare ribs and skinny udders up to the age of fourteen to eighteen months. Between the age of three months and eighteen months unless you feel a little ashamed to show your dairy young stock to your friends and visitors, you may be sure they are too fat for development as successful milking cows.

Big bellies must be developed if the animal is to grow into a cow capable of dealing with large quantities of food. This can best be done by feeding large quantities of bulky, but nutritional food, and limiting fat and flesh-making concentrates.

Bare ribs are an indication that the animal is using all its food for growth instead of putting on surplus flesh. But this does not mean the calf must be starved. Growth should be maintained throughout but the ribs should always be capable of being counted without handling them. This means that they must be seen and not flesh-covered so that they are individually indistinguishable, except, of course, when the thick winter hair growth covers them.

If good grass, hay and/or silage is available, and, with calves over six months old, oat straw for belly filling, there is no need to feed concentrates of any kind, and when the calf becomes a cow she will have a better digestion as a result. In cattle, as in humans, it is the concentrated manufactured and processed foods which damage the digestion, and the longer the stomach can be kept free of such foods the healthier will the system remain and the more capable will it be of coping with a period of strain should it be necessary during the cowhood milking life.

Flesh or fat on a young heifer's udder is a sure indication of a potentially poor yielder. The udder at all stages of growth to cowhood should be loose and silky, rather than formed and fleshy. Hard living will help this; overfeeding will put flesh and fat around the udder which will always be an impediment to profitable milk production.

Bull calves which are to be reared for breeding need a higher level of nutrition than the heifer calf. My experience is that a heifer calf fed on *more* than 130 gallons of milk, spread over five months or so, will rarely become a really efficient milk producer. That extra milk seems to make all the difference between an animal which acquires the ability to put on flesh and one which produces a large quantity of milk efficiently. But with a bull calf it is different, at any rate up to a maximum of about 180 gallons of milk given at the rate of a gallon or so daily for six to eight months according to the size and breed of the calf, and of course suckled from the cow every time. But it is still possible to ruin even a bull calf with too much food of a fattening nature. A successful Hereford breeder I know went in for Jersey cattle and decided to prepare his first Jersey bull for show. He turned out a magnificent animal, but though it started life as an extremely well-bred Jersey, it looked, apart from its colour, much more like a Hereford than a Jersey in the show ring.

It does demonstrate how important feeding is to the development of true breed characteristics, and how a really good inheritance can be made the most of, or marred beyond measure, by feeding. If underfeeding is practised to the detriment of the continuing growth of the calf a similar change in breed conformation may result, but overfeeding, especially between the ages of six months and maturity, is far more common, and in my opinion more harmful to the dairy calf.

The most important thing of all is to see that all the food the young animal has is its natural food, grown without chemical stimulants or poison sprays, and that if any supplements are given at all, they are natural and not synthetic. There is often need for a mineral and trace element addition to the normal diet, especially on land which has been depleted by years of chemical manuring, or years of extractive cropping without adequate organic manuring. But it is wise to avoid the synthetic mineral and trace element supplement, and use only natural herbs (in the leys or in dried form) or seaweed meals or powders which contain all the known minerals and trace elements in natural form.

If the bull calf is not to be reared for breeding, then, in the pure dairy breeds nothing can be gained from keeping it longer than the next convenient occasion for a journey to the slaughterhouse. (For the small difference in price which grading through the market brings for the calf, a shilling or two, I prefer the calf to escape the agonies of a day at the market with its inevitable cruelties; it is now possible for them to go direct to the slaughterhouse.) The cost in milk of getting the higher price of a veal calf is far greater than the gain.

When buying a bull calf for rearing avoid one which has been taken off milk and put on to a milk substitute or gruel. See that he is thriving on his dam or a foster mother and he should then be easy to transfer to the nurse cow which you will have waiting for him. Find out how much milk he is having and allow him a similar quantity when he arrives on your farm whether or not you feel it is too much or too little. Then any change in quantity that is to be made to adjust him to approximately a gallon a day, should

23. A heifer in good growing condition—Polden Autumn Gold.

24. Heifers should be kept in hard growing condition—without excess flesh.
A group at Goosegreen in the early Spring.

25. Some of the author's Polden Herd going out to graze. Note the capacious barrels essential to efficient dairy cows.

26. A group of the author's prize-winning Jerseys.

be made gradually. A sudden change of feeding, involving also a change of environment, will invariably result in digestive trouble and scouring.

If it is a Jersey calf, forget the fallacy that Jersey milk is too rich for a Jersey calf. Nature provided Jersey milk for the Jersey calf before ever man had the idea of using it for himself. The reason that many Jersey calves scour on Jersey milk is not because of its richness but because they are getting too much. Occasionally also, a calf will scour because it is getting too little and, in hunger, eats scraps of other food lying around the calf house, which it is unable to digest. As advised in the disease treatment section of this book, the first thing to do in case of scour is to stop all food, and proceed with the treatment. But in order to be sure that the calf is returned to the correct quantity of milk after treatment, while he or she is fasting, check the weight of milk being given by the foster mother, and if it is too much or too little, adjust it by changing the nurse cow if it is too little, or taking from the cow each day milk in excess of the calf's need.

But whether the future herd sire is bred on the farm or bought from another breeder at less than six months of age, the most important factor in his future working efficiency and health, and consequently the health and vigour of his progeny, is the way in which he is reared from birth. There is absolutely no substitute for mother's milk actually drawn from its mother, or a foster mother, by the newly born creature itself, from birth until it is old enough to be self-sufficient on solid food, whether the creature is a calf, a baby elephant or just the farmer's boy. In spite of the much advertised foods of royal babies and Royal Show winners, nothing has yet been found which gives the same vigour and disease immunity as mother's milk. There is a job here for scientific experimenters to compare several generations of entirely naturally suckled animals, with comparable ages and breeds of animals reared from an early age, for several generations, on the 'fortified' foods of modern science, which, though they may give the superficial splendour of apparent well-being, may at the same time be devitalizing the digestive ability of the stomach and the eliminative capacity of the intestines and preparing the certainty of stomach ulcers and constipation, or T.B. and Johne's disease in adult life. Until we can be certain beyond doubt that there is no connection between degenerative, digestive and intestinal troubles and the now widespread practice of unnatural rearing, the only wise course is to continue in the way which has succeeded in nature since life began, limiting any modifications on the commercial farm to those from which there is no economical escape, such, for instance, as using a nurse cow after the calf has spent the first week or so suckling its dam.

Chapter 11

HINTS FOR NEW HERDSMEN

Though in my introduction to this book I said I had assumed an elementary knowledge of dairy farming, there are some observations of fundamental importance, which are not to be found in the many books to which the beginner will turn for guidance. They fall into no special category of herdsmanship, but I think they are worth sharing in this short chapter, with those who are quite new to dairy herd management and with those experienced dairy farmers and herdsmen who may not hitherto have considered them of importance. Some are original; some have been acquired from men more experienced than I; others have been suggested to me by my own workers; all, though apparently elementary, are worth consideration, if the efficiency and health of the herd are to be maintained.

Stocking the Cow or Heifer

The right age to serve a heifer and the right stage of oestrum at which to put either a heifer or a cow to bull, are matters for conjecture among all breeders, novice or expert. Even the experts vary in their pronouncements on the subject.

Theoretically the optimum age for a heifer to be served is the stage shortly after a marked natural decelleration of growth takes place and the sexual characteristics noticeably develop. One would expect this stage to coincide with the start of oestrum, in other words at puberty. No doubt under natural conditions this is so, and the heifer accepts the bull at one of her first 'heats'. The optimum period for the most profitable milk yield is probably rather later. It varies with the breed and it varies with the strains within the breed. But in my experience of the pure dairy breeds it comes somewhere between the ages of fifteen and eighteen months.

If nutrition in the first six months of life has been adequate, it is probably right to serve the pure dairy heifer about midway through the third six months of life—at about fifteen months old. Invariably if service is left until twenty months or so, subsequent lifetime milk production suffers, not only in the longer period of unproductive life, but in the lower annual yield once production has started.

There is a point at which the heifer's system has completed normal growth and diverts the food which is in excess of maintenance requirements, either to putting on flesh or producing milk. If this point is passed without the animal having started milk production, the process of conversion of foodstuffs into body flesh and fat commences, and for some obscure reason it is not easy to change it back to a process of conversion to milk. The ideal, then, is for the birth of the calf to coincide with this change in the emphasis of metabolism, and in my experience this point comes at about two years of age in the normally developed dairy female.

The optimum stage of oestrum at which the actual service should take place is unlikely ever to be known by man, though it may well be guessed at. Artificial insemination stations are carrying on experiments which will produce some theoretical data on this subject. But the truth of the matter, in my opinion, is likely to remain for ever a secret between the bull and the cow. The ideal way of achieving insemination, under optimum conditions therefore, is to run the bull with the heifers or cows. This system has many objections in the commercial herd, because of difficulties of observing and recording all services. But it has the advantage of certainty, especially with heifers, which cannot always be seen to be 'bulling'. I remember in the early days of my cattle breeding, I ran a bull with ten heifers from November to the time they turned out to grass, from the yard in which they were wintered.

I did not see one of these heifers served nor did I see one 'bulling'. I assumed that they were suffering from some complaint which prevented them from coming on heat. I called in a veterinary surgeon during the spring and asked if he could do anything to bring the heifers on heat so that I could get them served. He examined them, decided they were not in calf, though it was in any case difficult to be sure, but as I had not seen a single one of them on heat he injected them with a hormone to bring them on heat. Every one of them proved to have been in calf to December and January services. The effect of the injection was to cause most of them to abort the calves they were carrying. The bull had done his job at the right time, and neither he nor the heifers had thought it necessary to give me any information about their relationship!

I would not have got any one of those heifers in calf had the bull not run with them. Since then I have always run a bull with my heifers and though they are closely observed every day a large proportion of them are served when the bull thinks fit, without our knowledge.

The nearest approach to this ideal system that can be achieved in the milking herd, is to allow the bulls to spend several hours with the cows they are to serve. In spite of the growing practice and insistent claims of artificial insemination, I believe the period of play between the cow and the bull has some useful purpose other than the pleasure of the animals themselves, just as the contact of male and female at the time of service has some object other than mere insemination. If nature had intended this contact for no other purpose than the insemination of the female, she would have made the cow bi-sexual as is the case with some other species. The fact is that the play period, and the actual contact at service, stimulates the secretion of hormones, probably as yet unidentified by man, which have an essential function in the perfect union of male and female and the ultimate success of the pregnancy and parturition, and may be even the eventual health and productive ability of the progeny.

Dual or Single-Purpose Breeds

Perhaps the greatest problem to the farmer contemplating pedigree breeding for the first time is the eternal controversy of the breeds 'having your cake and eating it,' or in other words the duel of the dual and single-purpose breeds. The emphasis on beef production which Government price manipulation has recently given, has provided a new lease of life to the fallacy that it pays better to produce milk from animals that are themselves capable of fattening when the profitable milking life is ended, and which give a bull calf that is worth £5 instead of 30s. or which can be reared for beef. Nobody who ever sat down to think this question out ever remained seated for long without kicking himself hard out of it for ever entertaining a doubt. The merest child knows that a cow that can produce a fat carcass at the end of her milking life, carries costly flesh every year of her milking life and robs the foodstuffs bin to do it. Furthermore, it is difficult enough breeding for one characteristic—milk or beef—but it is impossible to breed for both. And no one can forecast in the average dual-purpose herd, which the newly born calf is to be best for, until it has done at least one lactation, by which time considerable loss may already have occurred. But let me illustrate this argument by some official figures.

In Appendix IV of *The Milch Cow in England* (Faber), E. R. Coch-rane gives the average yields of full year recorded cows as follows, in relation to liveweight (1936–7 averages).

94

	Liveweight	Yields	Yield F.C. per 1,000 lb. Live-weight
	lb.		
Ayrshire	1,050	7,487	6,925
Friesian	1,300	9,167	6,300
Guernsey	915	6,805	7,625
Jersey	825	6,575	9,250
Red Poll	1,150	6,310	5,965
Lincoln Red	1,350	5,385	5,150
Shorthorn	1,250	5,715	5,395

Thus calculating on official National Average yields of 4 percent fat-corrected milk per 1,000 lb. liveweight, that if the Jersey is 100 percent efficient in production, the breeds are efficient in the following percentages:

	percent
Jersey	100
Guernsey	$82\frac{1}{2}$
Ayrshire	75
Friesian	68
Red Poll	$64\frac{1}{2}$
Shorthorn	58
Lincoln Red	56

On 1951 yields the Red Polls and Shorthorns have shown a 15 percent yield increase over 1936–7 compared with 10 percent in the Jersey and Ayrshire average, and 1 percent only in the Friesian breed; but this still leaves the dual-purpose cow only 65 percent efficient compared with my single-purpose Jersey.

Assuming the height of efficiency for a cow's production to be £150 a year we find therefore that 6 years' milk production for a Jersey equals £900; 6 years' milk production for a dual-purpose cow £585—a deficit of £315 a cow in a very modest milking life. It is an impossible margin for the dual-purpose animal to make good by means of the greater value of the dual-purpose bull calves and the cow's own carcass at the end of her milking life. I should like the dual-purpose advocate to show me how this deficit is to be made up, even with to-day's weighting of prices in favour of beef production. And I would urge the beginner who is tempted to take an each-way bet on a dual purpose breed, to be sure he knows how it can be done before he starts herdsmanship with a certain leakage of 35 percent efficiency from the start. It won't take many years of 35 percent leakage to run away with 100 percent of the capital of even the best-breeched beginner.

Calving

Don't assist the cow until it is clear that she needs it.

As soon as the calf is born see that it can, and does, breathe freely. If it appears normal nothing need be done. If not, open the mouth and remove any mucus. Take one jaw in each hand, hold them apart and blow sharply down the throat. This will clear the throat, cause the calf to gasp and take air into the lungs which has to be exhaled —thus breathing will commence if it has not already done so. Repeat this blowing down the throat several times until the calf is breathing. Artificial respiration may be applied by gentle pressure on the ribs of the chest—at the same time rubbing the calf vigorously all over to stimulate circulation.

Then leave the calf to be licked by the cow.

The calf should find its own food after an hour or two. Draw the cow's teats to free the flow of milk and see that the teats are easily capable of being drawn from by the calf. If after about six hours the calf has not been seen to suckle the cow some assistance should be given.

For the first forty-eight hours after the cow calves take no more milk from the cow than is necessary for the calf, and to relieve pressure in the udder.

The cow will need little or no food for twenty-four hours. A bran mash, made with molasses, will help in case of constipation which sometimes precedes or follows calving, especially where concentrated feeding has been given. Water should be available as and when the cow needs it.

The cow may be allowed to eat all but the coarsest and most fibrous of the placenta if she wishes. It provides valuable hormones which she may need. Leave the decision as to whether she needs them to the cow herself. But watch that she doesn't choke.

Getting a Cow out of a Ditch

As one who has farmed for twelve years surrounded by Somerset rhines (the deep, wide ditches which intersect and drain the flat lowlands of Somerset) I write with feeling about getting a cow out of a ditch. I hadn't been in Somerset long before I had to learn from one of my men how to fish for cows!

The fixed loop of a strong cart-rope around the neck should be attached to a point on a cart, trailer or tractor, well above the bank of the ditch, so that when the rope is strained the tendency is for the rope to raise the head. Clear the bank with a spade if necessary so that there are no obstacles. Move the horse or tractor away slowly, seeing that the cow is moving smoothly up the bank. A slow steady pull will get her out without damage. There is no risk of a broken neck. A cow's neck is the best place to attach a rope in pulling her out of a hole of any kind—never the horns, which would break off.

In pulling a horse, on the other hand, attach the rope around the shoulders and under the front legs—never around the neck which, unlike the cow's, will break.

The Bull

Enough has been said in recent years condemning the old-fashioned methods of bull management. The basic needs of the bull are now catered for by all thoughtful farmers. Yet I still see bulls tied in the darkest corner of the cowshed, throughout the four seasons of the year, by farmers who are governed by panic in the presence of a bull, and the belief that the most valuable animal on the farm can be kept under control only if he is subdued by fear. Only a few years ago I met a farmer who, each time he returned his Shorthorn bull from serving a cow, beat him with a stick and tied him up in his dark corner again, 'just to show him who was boss'. The bull did not dispute the farmer's demonstration of superiority for some years, for he was always tied by the chain round his neck and the ring in his nose, while it was performed. But one day he managed to slip his chain for the only few minutes' freedom of his life, and the farmer now carries a permanent reminder in the shape of a crippled hip, as to who eventually proved to be boss.

The first essential for a bull is ample exercise. A bull which is handled daily from calfhood will rarely become difficult to manage. It is false economy of the worst type to miss the bull's daily walk, especially nowadays when machinery is so depriving the cowman of his exercise! For the health and happiness of the bull and for the good of the herdsman a 15 or 20 minutes' walk on a hard road (to keep the feet in good trim) is the finest medicine on the farm.

In housing the bull, provide him with a clear view of activity. He is, unlike the herdsman, not given to daydreams about fair damsels, his imagination extends only to the heifer in his eye, so let him see her and he will trust you to bring her to him when his services are needed. But if he is confined out of sight of the rest of the herd, the day may well come when he loses interest in his work.

Ringing a Young Bull

It is the law that all bulls of 10 months of age and over must have a ring through the nose. As ten months is the age to get him licensed by the Ministry of Agriculture Livestock Officer, he need not be rung until he is licensed for use. The bull ring is hinged and may be opened for insertion through the thin membrane between the two nostrils. An ordinary steel (as used for sharpening carving knives) may be jabbed through the nose at that point with only momentary pain for the young bull, and hardly any bleeding. The steel makes a cleaner hole, through which the ring can be passed, closed and screwed together, than a sharp instrument.

Leading a Bull

The best way to lead a bull is from a chain which runs up through the ring and is clipped with a spring hook to a strap around the base of the two horns. This gives all the control that is possible for one man, and if he holds the chain close to the head the leverage from the horns to the nose, when the chain is pulled backwards, will halt or steady the bull, unless his nose has been allowed to toughen by tying or leading direct from the nose ring. Direct attachment to the ring should be avoided as it toughens the nose and deadens control. Whilst the nose remains tender, control of the bull is complete. Use of a pole, which we discarded many years ago, has the effect of toughening the nose and the bull may then jerk it out of the man's hand.

Where two men are leading the bull, even better control may be maintained with two chains on straps from the head or horn strap down through the ring and out horizontally to a man on either side.

This is the ideal way of parading a bull in the show ring. He can be led on a straight course with his head exactly at the desired level, by keeping the leads taut. If the bull tends to move in the wrong direction he may be checked by a pull from the man on the other side, yet his movement in that direction is limited by the other man. When leading the bull at a show it is easier for the judge to examine him when the men walk at the end of each lead, well away from the bull.

Some Words Explained

Some expressions in common usage among herdsmen and cattle breeders in talking of their cattle are not self-explanatory and need elaborating for the novice.

QUALITY. Fine bone, thin skin, bright colour and the general appearance which go to make up the superior fineness of a thoroughbred horse, or a Jersey cow, compared with coarse breeds of either species.

TYPE. A word which has come into use to cover all the requirements of conformation and character, as distinct from known productive ability, and accepted by each breed society as the ideal of its breed.

CONSTITUTION, is a combination of all the factors which make for health and ability to withstand, indeed to enjoy, hard work, as evidenced in a strong symmetrical body with large heart, lung and stomach capacity, wide ribs, deep body, especially chest, supported by firm, squarely placed legs.

SPRING OF RIB. The spring refers to the angle at which the ribs are offset from the backbone. Ribs offset at a wide angle from the backbone leave large capacity for the internal organs, especially stomachs, of the body. This is called good spring of rib.

SPRINGING. The freshening signs of imminent calving. A cow or heifer is said to be 'springing' to calve when the udder begins to enlarge, the vulva softens and enlarges, and the barrel shows the width and fullness of advanced pregnancy.

BARREL, is the term used to describe the trunk of the cow or the barrel-shaped portion of the body between the shoulders and the hips.

ESCUTCHEON, the reversed hair covering on the skin between the udder and the vulva (the portion of the cow's generative organs visible externally). A Frenchman, F. Guenon, expounded a theory which claimed to estimate a cow's productive ability from the pattern made by the escutcheon hair. (See Guenon's *Theory of the Escutcheon* in his book, *Milch Cows,* published by Orange Judd, Publishing Co., Inc., New York.)

TOPLINE. The line from the shoulder to the tail setting along the centre of the animal's back. Ideally it should be horizontally straight. Any rise or fall in the line as viewed from the side of the cow (standing back a few yards) is indicative of a weakness.

SWITCH. The long hair at the end of the tail.

Section Four

CATTLE DISEASES — THEIR PREVENTION AND TREATMENT

Chapter 12

'THERE'S ONLY ONE DISEASE
OF ANIMALS. . .'

I left university with the deep bewilderment about animal diseases, which I imagine is common to all agricultural and veterinary students. The only certain thing about animal diseases seemed to be man's inability to prevent or cure most of them. It was not until I had experienced these diseases in my own herd and started at the beginning in my attempt to eliminate and prevent them, instead of accepting the diseases and treating them as inevitable, that I discovered the root cause of most of them. Until in fact I discovered that there is only one disease of animals and its name is man!

The solution was then simple. If I could get the animals back to a life as nearly as economically practicable to what it was before man perverted them to his own use, and provide them as fully as possible with all the requirements of health available under natural conditions, it was reasonable to assume that health would be restored and maintained.

That in fact has been my experience, and in this section of the book I publish the treatments evolved from this assumption, which have been proved effective when used by farmers themselves on their own cattle in all parts of the world.

But first let me give you some of my experiences which led to the discovery of the simple natural cures for diseases which have hitherto seemed incurable by the involved methods of orthodox veterinary science. I have previously written about the diseases which drained my resources and nearly ruined two herds of cattle; how artificial manures were dispensed with entirely and how manuring entirely by natural means and feeding my cattle mainly on organically grown food and herbs, I restored my herd and my farm to health and abundance from the stage when 75 percent of my animals were suffering from contagious abortion, sterility, tuberculosis and mastitis.

PREVENTION & TREATMENT OF CATTLE DISEASES

I spent large sums of money on vaccination and the orthodox veterinary treatment of sterility, and the only result was increasing disease. Some cows aborted their calves as often as three times after being vaccinated, and one after another the cows were declared by the veterinary surgeon to be useless and incapable of further breeding after he had applied a succession of orthodox treatments and failed. He told me that I should never be safe from these diseases until I adopted a system of regular vaccination of all my cattle as they reached the age of six months; I must also fatten and sell the sterile animals and tuberculosis reactors. In spite of pressure, I resisted all this advice, largely because I had not the capital to replace the 'useless' animals which I was advised to dispose of, and partly because I was in any case becoming convinced that we had been tackling disease from the wrong end.

When 25 percent of my cattle continued normal and healthy lives in the midst of millions of bacteria of all kinds, I became convinced that the much-maligned bacteria were not the primary factor in the cause of disease. After many years' working on that assumption, with the gradual elimination of so-called contagious diseases from my farm, although I am regularly taking diseased animals in for treatment, I have reached the conclusion that bacteria are not only *not* the main cause of disease, or abnormality in the body, but Nature's chief means of combating it. What we choose to call harmful bacteria are ineffective or inactive except where the abnormal conditions exist to make their work necessary. If we allow them their natural function, to clear up a diseased condition, and do not continue the malpractices which gave rise to the abnormality, leaving the body entirely free of external sustenance until the cleansing work of the bacteria is done, correcting deficiencies only with natural herbs, and then only introducing the patient to natural food grown with organic manuring, good health is the natural outcome.

In experimenting with that disease of the cow's udder, mastitis, I have taken the discharges of cows suffering from it and applied the virulent bacteria to the udders of healthy cows, with no ill effect whatever to the healthy cow. This is a disease which is said to be spread from one cow to another by invasion of the udder with bacilli. Strict germicidal measures are claimed to be the most effective form of prevention and treatment, yet mastitis is costing the farmer more and more every year.

My own cows suffered most severely with this disease when everything to do with them was almost continuously submerged in disinfectant and when I was using all the orthodox treatments. Every farmer knows that his cows *will* get mastitis under orthodox methods of management and would continue to do so even were they kept under glass cases. The fact is that this disease is merely a catarrhal condition of the udder, brought about by feeding cows for high yields on foods in which the natural elements, vitamins and plant hormones, essential to proper endocrine functioning, either never existed because the food was grown from a soil dying of chemical poisoning or in other ways deficient, or were removed in the process of manufacture.

For many years now my farm has been manured exclusively by natural means, and the animals fed almost exclusively on naturally grown crops.

Kept under this régime, the sterile animals I was advised to have slaughtered have come back to breeding again and formerly useless cattle have been turned into a valuable pedigree herd, the only cost being hard work and a respect for Nature. Had I taken the veterinary surgeon's advice I should have been ruined.

Encouraged by success with my own animals I advertised for other farmers' rejects, particularly those that had been declared incapable of breeding by veterinary surgeons. Regularly, now, I am curing these cows with which orthodox treatment has failed, and only in cases where physiological defects prevent breeding has cure been impossible.

Similarly with tuberculosis, I have reclaimed reactors which would otherwise have been useless. All my work indicates that tuberculosis can permanently be prevented and, in its early stages, cured on food grown in properly managed soil, provided an adequate diet of mineral-rich herbs is given.

Magnesium deficiency, which is a disease arising from the destruction by potassic manures of a trace element in the soil, has been cured at Goosegreen Farm. One animal suffering from this deficiency lay stretched out as though dead for ten days. By a course of warm water enemas, plain water drinks and no foods until the animal was so emaciated that some sustenance was indicated, then introducing diluted molasses and fresh mineral-rich green food, I got the animal back to health. She has since given me several strong calves, 900 gallons of milk in each of two lactations, in spite of her ten-days coma and fast.

Such were the experiences which led me to experiment extensively with herbal treatments for cattle and other animals. In the study of veterinary herbs, I have had much assistance from Juliette de Bairacli Levy (author of *Complete Herbal Handbook for Farm and Stable* (Faber), *Medicinal Herbs—Their Use in Canine Ailments,* and *The*

Cure of Canine Distemper and Hard Pad, etc.), whose successes in the use of veterinary herbs are world renowned.

In the following pages I have set out treatments which I have proven time and time again and which are being carried out by farmers themselves at little cost on their own farms. I have dealt only with diseases with which I have had successful results, and which I know can be treated by farmers themselves. Any disease for which I am unable to offer a simple cure, I have omitted from this book, though this does not mean that such diseases are *not* capable of treatment by natural means.

The following sections are intended to enable cattle breeders to cope with the more common cattle diseases until such time as they are able to get their farms and their herds established in organic methods of management.

All the treatments assume immediate action at the first sign of abnormality in the animal's condition. Any delay is likely to render the treatment less effective. I deal here only with prevention and treatment. The main diseases and their causes are discussed at greater length in *Fertility Farming.*

ABORTION

Abortion, or premature expulsion of the foetus, is part of the natural elimination of toxins from an overloaded system, and as such is altogether beneficial to the ultimate health of the animal. The loss of the calf should not be regarded as a disaster, but as a life-saver for the dam, which might otherwise become permanently sterile, and incapable of further useful existence on the farm. As it is, with orthodox treatment, she will probably become at least temporarily sterile and if the bad feeding which caused the toxaemia continues, permanent sterility, or other serious toxic condition is almost certain.

But with enlightened management and organic treatment the act of abortion becomes a healing process in the life of the animal whose subsequent health and productive ability will be wonderfully benefited as a result.

Prevention

Prevention is rarely possible once the obvious symptoms are observed. But provided organic methods are the rule on the farm, it is possible, immediately impending abortion is suspected, to commence treatment which may avert an actual abortion.

27 and 28. Intelligent and dairy-like heads. Polden Summer Storm (Jersey) and Pimhill Canty (Ayrshire).

29. Ramsons or Wild Garlic (*Allium Ursinum*) growing. The most valuable herb in the treatment and prevention of cattle diseases.

30. Dosing with garlic tablets made from wild garlic.

As with all toxic conditions, fasting is the immediate necessity. After the first twenty-four hours without food, as it may encourage expulsion of the foetus, it is not possible to give the usual enema, and some form of gentle herbal purgative should be given. The liquid from twelve senna pods soaked overnight in two pints of warm water should be given as a drench on the morning and night of the second day of the fast and repeated on the third day. Alternatively twelve rhubarb-root tablets.

As abortion is basically a catarrhal condition, the best possible cleanser is garlic in some form. If garlic grows wild on the farm, then whole plants should be gathered and fed at the rate of four whole plants daily for two weeks, but commencing with one only on the first day increasing by one each day. If no wild garlic is available, four flaked bulbs of garden garlic may be fed morning and night, similarly commencing with one only the first morning and increasing to a daily ration of four bulbs morning and night. If the cow will not readily take the flaked bulbs, or even the whole garlic plants (which is unlikely as her system will be demanding it), it may be chopped and mixed with a little kale or silage or other appetizing food and a little molasses.

Failing either garlic plant or root, the prepared tablets of whole crushed garlic may be used, giving six tablets in a little water morning and night. The tablets need not dissolve. The water is merely to assist passage of the tablets to the stomach where they will dissolve and achieve digestion slowly, at the same time penetrating the whole system and purifying the unclean places.

During the fast the animal should be kept in and allowed access to ample clean water, which should not be from a tap if possible. Spring, stream or well water is preferable for an animal in normal health, and even more so for a sick animal, as it contains vital elements not present in the dead chlorinated water of the Rural District Council.

The fast should be continued for a week or until signs of impending abortion are passed. At the end of three days if there is no worsening of the condition molasses should be fed, commencing with a pint on the first day increasing by one pint daily up to two pints morning and night. This should be given as a drench diluted in warm water to a consistency which makes it capable of being poured from a bottle. The genuine cane molasses should be used.

If after a week the animal appears to be happy and normal, organically grown green food may be introduced in small quantities, gradually increasing to normal rations of twenty or thirty pounds of good kale, and at the end of the second week a small bran mash—3-4 lb. of bran—may be given with added molasses.

Treatment After Abortion

If, in spite of all preventive efforts, the animal aborts, or if, as so often happens, abortion has taken place without the warnings having been observed, then the only treatment is one that takes advantage of the natural cleansing process which has been commenced, to take the opportunity of getting the animal back to a condition of normal health in which she may enjoy healthy pregnancy in the future.

Immediate action for the cow should be to provide, if possible, the natural stimulus of a calf. If a young calf is available this should be put to suckle the cow at once. This will help to stimulate the normal hormone secretions which have a cleansing effect on the uterus, and which are responsible for milk flow and udder health. The calf should be left with the cow day and night and allowed to suckle at will. If the cow does not take readily to the calf she must be trained by holding three times a day until the calf may be left to help itself. The suckling calf is by far the best treatment for any abnormal calving or udder troubles, as it calls forth the endocrine secretions of the ductless glands—called hormones—which play a major part in the maintenance of health in the organs of reproduction and milk production, and adjust the abnormalities which artificial treatment may have caused.

Then, after a week or two of suckling the treatment for sterility should be followed (see page 131).

ACETONAEMIA

Of recent years, coinciding with the more widespread adoption of forcing methods of feeding cattle for milk, the complaint known as acetonaemia has become much more frequent. There are few high-yielding herds practising modern methods of 'steaming-up' and high protein feeding, which do not have regular cases of this disease.

Acetonaemia is closely related to the high feeding which precedes calving in the attempt to build up a heavy yielding cow, and more especially in the even more common forcing with high protein foods, of a cow which after calving shows heavy milking potentialities and is consequently fed to the very maximum of her production.

I have only had two cases in my own herd; the first we lost through inexperience, in spite of early veterinary treatment of an orthodox nature, the second, which I cured myself. Both were animals which calved down, giving exceptionally high yields of milk, in support of which I was tempted to feed high protein foods to excess. Like most cattle breeders, in those days the higher the potential yield of a cow the higher I tried to force it.

But I have treated a number of cases for other people, and am hearing of an increasing number of cattle which farmers are treating themselves by an early adoption of the simple treatment set out below.

The cow goes off her food and her breath has an odour of acetone, a sweet but sickly smell like peardrops, indicating an attempt on the part of the system to remove excess acetone from the blood stream. The danger period is some two or three weeks after calving, when the results of excessive protein feeding have had an opportunity to take effect.

Prevention

The best prevention, as with milk fever, is a considerable lowering or even a complete withholding of concentrate feeding for two weeks before and after calving. Certainly where a cow is known to have a tendency to acetonaemia or milk fever, protein foods should be reduced to the lowest level for the weeks before and after calving. In the summer when grass growth is lush, the cow should be taken off the best leys and put on to a poor pasture or brought into a loose-box and given hay and bran mashes, until it is seen that she is well over the strain of calving. Then she may gradually be introduced to the production ration which will build up the yield slowly to what may be assumed to be the normal productive capacity of the animal.

Treatment

Acetonaemia is due to an excessive intake of protein and can therefore to some extent be adjusted by the use of a concentrated carbohydrate treatment, but the immediate essential is to encourage natural elimination and the self-correction of the protein unbalance by the animal herself. This can be done by immediate fasting, followed by the feeding of a mineral-rich low-protein gruel made with molasses and powdered treebarks, until such time as the breath once more smells normal, and the animal shows interest in bran mash and a little hay.

During the fast the vitamin value of green food may be obtained without the overstimulating effect of the protein in grass and other green foods, by the use of extracts of grasses and herbs. Leaf plasma tablets are now available which contain the extracts of grasses, nettles, cleavers and other herbs and these may be used to maintain the resistance of the animal during a fast. Four tablets morning and night is the appropriate dose in most cases.

During a fast of longer than two days I have found it necessary to give rectal enemas, for once the intestines are empty and no solid food is being taken by the cow, peristaltic action ceases, and any poisons which are discharged into the intestines are in danger of being reabsorbed if they are not removed by means of the enema. Once solid food is being taken again, and the dung is being passed in a normal consistency, enemas may cease.

The first food may be in the form of small bran mashes and then a little hay. Though in most fasting cases green food is the best introduction to food, in the case of acetonaemia it is well to avoid even the protein of green food until the digestive system has had an opportunity of settling down again. After a few days of bran mashes (five pounds of bran morning and night, and a handful of hay midday) kale or cabbage may be introduced slowly. But any tendency to be disinterested in food should be the sign for a resumption of the fasting and enemas, for this will be a sure sign that the fast was broken before the cow was ready.

ACTINOMYCOSIS OR WOODEN TONGUE

Actinomycosis is the name given to a growth which develops generally in the throat or mouth of the animal, especially the base of the tongue or the side or under portion of the jaw, but which may also be found in other parts of the body. The name actinomycosis derives from the belief that it is caused by a ray fungus and is based on the Greek translation of the words ray fungus.

The real cause of the trouble is a deficiency, particularly of iodine and other trace elements, resulting in the fungus growth, which if not checked may prevent the animal from eating or chewing its cud.

Fortunately the onset of the disease is slow, and it may therefore be eliminated by a slow correction of the deficiencies, in conjunction with a cleansing treatment designed to tone up the animal's system to encourage the quick assimilation of its natural health requirements, and the self absorption of the offending fungal growth.

Prevention

The best prevention is a diet rich in organic minerals and trace elements, obtained by feeding on home-grown foods grown on organically manured soil, and particularly on pastures which contain a high proportion of deep-rooting herbs. A case of actinomycosis is extremely rare on cattle living mainly on the produce of herbal leys; I have never heard of such a case and I doubt if herbal leys of long standing in which the roots of the herbs have had ample opportunity to penetrate to the source of trace elements absent in the topsoil, would ever permit such a disease. There is no doubt that the herbal ley is the best preventive of this as well as many other diseases.

But as an additional safeguard, and in cases where the herbal ley is not established, the feeding of small quantities of seaweed powder or the new seaweed foods will provide all the minerals and trace elements necessary to prevent this and other deficiency diseases.

Treatment

Where the growth has commenced, treatment should first of all aim at allowing the system to adjust itself to the process of eliminating the foreign matter which it has localized at the seat of the growth. This is done by a two-day fast on molasses and water only, with strong doses of garlic. This is then followed by a slow building up of the iodine content of the system by means of a blend of the medicinal seaweeds such as Irish moss, Iceland moss, sea holly and bladderwrack.

On the first and second days of the fast give one pint only of molasses diluted in warm water to enable it to be poured down the throat of the animal and administered as two drenches morning and night. Six garlic tablets should be added morning and night to the molasses drench.

On the evening of the second day give the same drench but with the addition of two tablespoonfuls of seaweed powder. This should continue to be given morning and night for a further four or five days, or until the growth appears to be diminishing. The molasses may be gradually increased to two pints daily as the fast proceeds, and at the end of a week the animal may be introduced to green food of some kind, slowly increasing it to a normal daily ration for maintenance purposes.

Even when a cure is effected it is wise to continue a daily inclusion of one dessertspoonful of the seaweed powder or the inclusion of 10 percent of seaweed cubes in the ration, to prevent the recurrence of wooden tongue.

BLOWN, BLOAT, OR HOVEN

Blown, which is also known as bloat or hoven, is the condition in which gases collect in the first stomach of the cow and if not stopped may cause distention of the stomach to the extent of asphyxiation and death.

The trouble is generally at its most prevalent during early spring or summer when the cattle first go to graze lush leys or pastures, and the orthodox explanation is that an excessive ingestation of green food, particularly clover, is the cause. But all curative and preventive measures which have worked on this assumption have so far failed.

Though clover is an important factor it is, I believe, a secondary factor. It is not necessary for the cow to overeat to become blown. The danger is from the production of gases in the stomach and not from gorging. A cow will normally stop eating when her stomach is full. With Blown, gases are produced causing the stomach to distend long before the stomach is full of food. I have investigated internally many animals which have died from this trouble and find that in practically every case there has been some undigested stale concentrate food present in the stomach, and though only a minute quantity, it has been sufficient in combination with the clover, to start fermentation and the rapid production of gases. Most of the blown victims I have examined have been comparatively heavy milkers consuming large quantities of production ration—unnatural food which is not only difficult to digest but lacks the vitamins and minerals which aid digestion. It has been found that the production ration is rarely completely digested until a long spell of spring grazing has provided the necessary digestive tone to enable it to clear up arrears in the stomach. The result is that during the early part of the summer, while undigested food still remains in the system, the risk of blown is great. As the summer advances the risk becomes progressively less, not because the cow eats less clover, or eats less quickly, but because the accumulations of the winter have been disposed of, and nothing remains to set up fermentation. Later in the summer and early in the autumn the danger increases again as the concentrated production ration is increased and digestion becomes more difficult.

Prevention

If before the cow is put to grass, the stomach is completely emptied of stale food there will be nothing to cause fermentation. Fast the cows for twenty-four hours, especially if there is a known tendency to blowing, and if you can get hold of some charcoal in pieces about the size of a sixpence, or in tablet form, give four to six pieces to each animal. Charcoal is a wonderful thing for absorbing stomach gases and preventing fermentation.

The long-term prevention, which I have found to have a most remarkable effect in eliminating blowing in my own herd, is to see that all the pastures contain a high proportion of herbs and deep-rooting grasses. Late-flowering or broad red clovers should be kept to a minimum, not more than a total of three pounds per acre, where blowing is feared. The herbal ley has a remarkable effect in providing the minerals essential to efficient digestion, and also the coarser grazing which suits the stomach of the cow. Divide the leys into paddocks and graze the cows continuously at the rate of ten or twelve to the acre, rather than 'on and off'.

Treatment

When a cow becomes blown, the immediate treatment after confining her without food, is to give a pint of linseed oil, and if you have them, four charcoal tablets, repeating them every half-hour until the trouble has gone. Keep the animal on the move to assist the movement of gas, and to prevent her from lying down.

Where the distention of the stomach is causing obvious discomfort and appears likely to increase, the stomach should at once be pierced with a trocar and canular, or if this instrument is not available, an ordinary penknife. The point at which to pierce should be the highest point of the distended stomach, midway between the last rib and the hip bone—approximately a hand span from each to the highest point of the distention. Jab the knife or instrument sharply in to its full extent and move it about to ease the passage of gas.

Another means of getting gases to move is to make a twisted rope of hay or straw and push it as far as possible down the back of the cow's mouth, though preventing it from going down her throat. Some of her own dung thrust into the cow's mouth will encourage her to chew in an attempt to be rid of it, and this, in addition to the rope down the mouth, will encourage the escape of gases. Additionally insert a rubber tube, the thin milk tube of a milking machine is ideal, into the anus as far as possible and keep this moving to assist the escape of gas and dung from the rear end.

Once an animal has been blown she must have at least a twenty-four hour fast before she is put to grass again. A large quantity of charcoal in some form will help to clear up remaining gases and fermenting foods during the fast.

CALF SCOUR

The immediate treatment, on the first sign of scour of any kind, is cessation of all food and the dosing with two garlic tablets.

Prevention

Where white scour appears in calves it is generally a result of wrong feeding, usually too high a proportion of protein in the food, or too much milk. Bacteria are quite secondary and are again Nature's means of dealing with dietary abnormality. Prevent by controlling milk intake to 5 or 6 lb. daily from a foster mother.

Treatment

Fast the calf for twenty-four hours on cold water only, and if the scour then appears to have diminished, reintroduce fresh whole milk diluted with equal parts of warm water. If the calf is sucking a cow, reintroduce small feeds of not more than three minutes' duration four times a day, preceded with a bottle of $1\frac{1}{2}$ pints cold water given as a drench, making certain the calf does not receive more than a maximum of six pints of milk during the day. Generally, with a calf that is sucking a cow, a half-gallon is sufficient, though with bucket feeding one gallon a day should be given, when the calf is once more in normal health.

If the scour is still bad after a twenty-four-hour fast, continue the fast a further day, allowing cold water only. If the scour then still persists, gentle warm water enemas of four pints, twice daily, are applied, reintroducing the calf to diluted milk after a maximum of two days' fasting which, with enemas, is sufficient to eliminate the scour completely.

HUSK OR HOOSE AND WORMS

Calves and young animals suffering from a husky cough in the late summer or early autumn may be suspected of Husk or Hoose caused by the lung worm. The eggs of the worm are picked up from the grass of dew or rain-washed pastures, hatch out in the lung and pass into the bronchial tubes from where they are coughed out to the ground again to continue their life cycle.

Prevention

Once the worms have gained a hold in grazing heifers, it is extremely difficult by any treatment, organic or chemical, to eradicate them. Great care should therefore be taken with young stock during late summer and early autumn. All young stock should be kept off permanent pastures or old leys (which carry many more eggs than the young ley) while the grass is wet, for the eggs are found in the dewdrops or raindrops on the blades of grasses and the leaves of clover. Where there is any risk of husk, bring younger cattle in on dewy or rainy nights in late summer and autumn. If the slightest husky cough is suspected, avoid further trouble by housing the group of cattle in which the cough is found, especially if the weather is showery. The only solution to the problem, which is often serious on old grassland, is to plough up the fields and sow them all down to young leys. In conjunction with ground limestone applications, this will get rid of the worms for many years. But even when this is done it is wise to keep the younger stock on the younger pastures.

Treatment

If the cough is taken early and the animals removed from pastures at once, fasting and drenching the system with garlic will eliminate the worms effectively and with considerable benefit to the general health of the animal. But if coughing is at all frequent and has reached the stage of prolonged and frequent bouts of coughing, there is little hope of completely clearing the trouble, and though the animal may live for months or even years, she will always fail to thrive and may eventually die from parasitic pneumonia. In early cases, confine the animal in a clean warm building, with ample ventilation, and withhold food of any kind. Even water should be omitted, if convenient. A heavy dose of garlic should be given—at least 15 tablets in a little water, and the garlic should be repeated every four hours during the fast which should last two days. At the end of the fast give the animal dry food only, hay and home-grown meal and 8 garlic tablets daily for a week, or until the cough seems to have gone. The aim is to keep the system thoroughly loaded with garlic, which not only eliminates the worms or their larvae, but also clears out the mucus in which they live.

Generous feeding should follow the fast in order to build up the natural resistance to parasitic attack in the future, and to throw off any worms which may still remain.

WORMS

For intestinal worms, the treatment is the same as for Husk except that green food and bran mashes should replace dry food for a week following the fast.

JOHNE'S DISEASE

The widespread incidence of Johne's disease among cattle coincided with the practice of feeding the calf on milk substitute, the general use of manufactured cattle foods of all kinds and the consequent deteriorating digestion of the animal. Far from being caused by a mysterious virus, (which is the usual explanation of any trouble for which there is no obvious cause), and for which there is no orthodox cure, Johne's disease really starts at calfhood with a weakening of the whole digestive system. Later in life, no doubt after a year or two of concentrated foods the cow suffers from incompletely digested food remaining in the intestines and setting up fermentation. If allowed to continue, this breaks down the mucous membrane of the intestines, and eventually the walls of the intestine. The corrugations which form on the walls of the intestine are an attempt on the part of the system naturally to localize the toxic wastes. Incomplete digestion causes, in the early stages an excessive appetite, but the continued intake of food to be added to the fermenting wastes already present, merely aggravates the condition and as the fermentation develops and inflammation of the mucous membrane sets in, loss of appetite follows with ultimate emaciation and death.

Prevention

The simple prevention of Johne's disease is a diet of natural foods, and if there is no alternative to the limited feeding of concentrated prepared foods then occasional fasting is necessary to enable the system to eliminate the residues of unnatural food which are never completely digested or absorbed by the body.

It is essential that the diet should contain a high proportion of fresh organically grown foods rich in vitamins, trace elements, and plant hormones, all of which are essential to complete digestion. It is probably the absence of these prerequisites of good digestion from the food

118

ingested, rather than the concentrated nature of the manufactured food itself, which is the real cause of the trouble. For it is not until the animal has had many months of unnatural food that she starts to scour—the first sign that the digestion is impaired. The feeding of food which does not supply the vital elements necessary to healthy digestion and assimilation and which in any case is difficult to digest by the bovine stomach designed for bulky foods, has a cumulative effect which the animal system eventually fails to cope with and the cow herself at last refuses food, when however, it is too late.

A herd which is naturally reared from birth—with calves suckled on cows an essential part of that rearing, (for nothing impairs the digestion more effectively than gruels and calf cake at an early age, though it may not become apparent until cowhood)—which is fed on organically grown bulky food with a high proportion of fresh grass or its nearest winter equivalent silage, tripodded hay, and kale, supplemented where necessary with herbs and organic minerals such as seaweed in some form, will never suffer from Johne's disease. But even in a herd so managed, any animal showing the first sign of digestive trouble, with scouring, should be fasted at once for at least twenty-four hours, or until normal again. This will eliminate any possibility of an accumulation of the causes of intestinal fermentation or inflammation.

Treatment

If for any reason Johne's disease has developed—provided the mucous membrane of the intestine is still sound and there is no sign of blood in the dung, it is possible to save the animal by keeping the whole alimentary tract free of food until it is quite clear of fermenting wastes. This may mean fasting the animal for one or two weeks, in which case daily enemas should be given with dosage of garlic, 6 tablets morning and night. After a week of complete fasting the animal may be given a gruel of powdered fenugreek seed with the addition of powdered treebarks available from veterinary herbal firms.

A two-pint gruel may be prepared by using a dessertspoonful of powdered fenugreek seed and a dessertspoonful of a powdered tree-barks blend (slippery American [red] elm and English elm barks), stirred into a smooth paste with an equal quantity of cane molasses, diluted with warm water. The powdered treebarks are available from herbalists. If a blend is not available, pure slippery elm bark will do—not slippery elm food, which is often diluted with flour.

This will form a soothing jelly-like gruel which will act as an internal poultice and assist the healing of the alimentary tract and at the same time provide an easily digested nutritive food.

The animal will live for weeks on this gruel—but after a week some solid green food may be tried if the dung appears to be of normal consistency. If the dung from this solid food continues to be passed in normal condition the animal may be assumed to be cured and the quantity of green food then gradually increased to normal. If diarrhoea again results then the fast on gruel should be continued for a further week—and so on until the animal is found to be able to deal with solid food.

The garlic should be continued daily indefinitely as an assistance to the elimination of mucus and the general purification of the blood stream. And a mineral rich diet from herbal leys and/or the addition to the diet of seaweed powder, is essential to the continued avoidance of Johne's disease.

JOINT-ILL

Joint-ill is not so frequent among calves as among foals. But it is a disease of calves, in which abscesses or thickenings form at the joints. Because of the frequent occurrence of an abscess at the navel or umbilicus, preceding or coinciding with the thickening of a joint of the leg or shoulder, it is believed that this disease is caused by germs which enter the body through the navel of the young animal at or shortly after the birth. Having had experience of joint-ill following the strictest possible precautions against infection through the navel, on farms where the calf is born in the cleanest possible conditions, and the navel disinfected immediately after birth, I do not accept this explanation as the primary cause. In my experience the disease is the result of a toxic condition in the dam, probably due to some deficiency in her feeding, the effects of which the calf's system attempts immediately to eliminate at birth. The calf thus develops an accumulation of pus at the navel, the only open point of discharge, and if elimination at this point fails, an accumulation at the joints follows. This joint swelling often occurs in adult animals suffering from similar toxic accumulations and is a common means employed by the system to localize poisons with a view to their ultimate elimination.

If the animal can be fasted immediately there is any sign of an abscess and supplied with the deficiency a speedy reduction of the swelling takes place. Usually, however, the swelling is not noticed until it has gained a considerable growth and with the very young animal it is then not possible to fast long enough to effect a speedy cure.

Prevention

I have found that this trouble responds to treatment with iodine in some form. This indicates that iodine deficiency is one of the causes. The most obvious preventative then is to see that the dam has an adequate supply of iodine in the diet during pregnancy. This is best supplied by the richest known source of organic iodine, seaweed, fed in powder or cube form, or as a long-term preventative, via the soil in the form of a top dressing of raw seaweed or compost made from or including seaweed.

Treatment

Immediately there is any sign of abnormality at the navel or any swelling at the joints of the knee, hocks, hips or shoulders, fast the calf on honey and water (a teaspoonful of honey in a pint of water three times a day). The fast should last for twenty-four hours if the trouble is caught at its commencement, or for two days if there is any considerable swelling. When milk is resumed continue with honey and water with addition of one teaspoonful seaweed powder morning and night.

During treatment the calf should have 2 garlic tablets morning and night and, if there is no evidence of normal dunging, 4 tablets of rhubarb root each night until the dung is normal. Alternatively, as an aid to intestinal movement, the liquid from the soaking for twelve hours, of 4 senna pods in a cupful of water, should be given as a drench.

MASTITIS

Mastitis is a catarrhal discharge thrown off by the cow's system at the point of greatest strain, and is the result of systemic toxaemia brought on by one of two factors. Either a diet which is not equal in its contents of the natural vitamins and plant hormones (which are the pre-requisites of the natural cleansing processes of healthy body secretions) to the output demands upon the cow; so the process breaks down; toxic catarrh replaces the natural hormone secretions of the mucous membrane of the udder. Or an excess of unnatural feeding causes the accumulation of toxic matter in various parts of the body which must be discharged in various ways, by mastitis, big knee, influenza or pneumonia, leucorrhoea (whites) or abortion, all of which result in a catarrhal discharge from one or other part of the body. In either case, if the excessive or inadequate feeding is continued, the trouble becomes chronic.

Prevention

If a period of fasting with frequent stripping and other efforts to eliminate mucus until the discharge ceases, is followed by a completely natural diet, devoid of artificial foods, and composed primarily of green foods, roots, hay, straw and silage, the trouble will clear itself, and in the process the cow will become healthier in every other respect. She may not give quite so much milk each lactation, but at least she will have many more healthy lactations, and any progeny she may bear will be one step nearer perfect health than she was herself.

Mechanical injury is, of course, another matter which cannot be expected to respond to natural treatment quite so quickly as mastitis caused by systemic toxaemia. Mastitis resulting from mechanical injury is usually the aftermath of bad machine milking or a blow from another cow. This is how the milking machine is wrongly blamed for udder trouble. In my experience, a milking machine cannot cause, or spread, udder trouble when properly used.

The fallacy that the machine spreads the disease may be discounted in the properly managed herd, for as I have previously stated, a healthy udder will not contract mastitis even when in contact with virulent bacteria. The bacteria cannot develop in the udder unless there is catarrhal material to be consumed.

Treatment

On first signs of abnormality in the milk or udder, stop all food and allow water only, until the milk becomes normal. Give a strong dose of garlic in some form and repeat it morning and night for a week or more. Two whole garlic plants chopped up and made into a ball with a little molasses and bran or 4 tablets of garlic fortified with the herb fenugreek. Milk out the affected quarter as often as possible, at least four times daily, but hourly if possible, or allow a calf to suckle it, making sure that it draws the affected quarter.

If there is any sign of inflammation in the udder apply alternate hot and cold fomentations, with massage, three times daily to the affected quarter or quarters until the inflammation goes, and during treatment finish off with a cold-water hose turned on to the udder and over the loins, for ten minutes, thoroughly soaking the region of the pelvis and udder. This stimulates a quick exchange of blood and speeds natural purification.

Work on the assumption that the mastitis is a catarrhal discharge resulting either from overfeeding, or feeding on a diet which is deficient in the vitamins and plant hormones essential to milk production. Fast the animal to give the body an opportunity to eliminate this catarrhal discharge naturally and assist this elimination by milking out the discharge as often as possible.

Continue the fast for as long as three days, giving a daily enema after the first day—after which if the milk is still not normal, a pint of cane molasses may be given diluted in warm water as a drench—divided into three doses daily for a further two days, but still without food. Continue the purifying garlic morning and night.

If the mastitis is caught soon enough such a long fast should not be necessary. Twenty-four hours is generally long enough if the animal has no food whatsoever.

When discharge has ceased, resume feeding with green food only— green food grown on composted land without any chemical manures. Continue feeding for a further week entirely on green food, without any concentrated food. She may then gradually be brought back to production ration—but not to excess.

The orthodox treatment is to *suppress* the discharge by means of penicillin or sulphonamides but unless the catarrh which causes the trouble is *eliminated* it will recur.

In addition to the feeding of natural food, rich in herbs providing the necessary minerals and plant hormones, a weekly dose of garlic, 4 whole plants or 6 tablets and a daily dessertspoonful of seaweed powder are excellent preventive measures.

MILK FEVER

Milk fever, though not strictly a fever, for there is rarely a high temperature, is commonly known as 'dropping after calving', though its technical name is parturient apoplexy. The symptoms are a restlessness, at any time from a few hours after calving up to four weeks or so after calving, in which the cow starts by raising first one hind leg and then the other in a paddling fashion and eventually collapses. She lies down and repeatedly turns her head back to her ribs. As the condition develops she will throw her head and the whole of her body back to the ground and may reach the stage of a coma, when if not attended to she will die.

Milk fever, perhaps more than any other disease, is the obvious result of over-exploitation of the cow. It is rarely found in poor milking cows and beef cattle, being confined almost entirely to dairy breeds and the heavier milking animals of those breeds. Further support of this theory is the fact that heifers never succumb to milk fever, and it is not until the cow has suffered two or three lactations of exploitation that she suffers. The third calving is usually the earliest time for milk fever.

It is caused by the strain on the system of the double stimulus of parturition and high protein feeding on the flow of milk. With a heavy milking cow the stimulus of calving on the flow of milk is already great. To add the additional stimulus of high feeding is too much for the cow, the flush of milk is so sudden and drains the blood stream and the ductless glands of all the requirements of milk production—various minerals, calcium and hormones—that the rest of the body almost ceases to function, and the cow collapses.

Prevention

Knowing that the cause is over-stimulation of the milk secretion, the prevention is simple and obvious—to reduce in all cases, and to cut out completely in cows known to have a tendency to milk fever, all foods likely to stimulate the flow of milk two weeks before calving. Feed in the ration during pregnancy a mineral-rich supplement which will build up the mineral reserves of the blood stream and the supply of hormones and in general bring the whole metabolism of the body to a high pitch of efficiency. The danger in high feeding is not so much the overfeeding of the animal, as the inefficiency of the cow's metabolism to cope with the diet. A diet rich in minerals and plant hormones is known to be beneficial to the animal metabolism. This may be achieved by the use of seaweed on the land and in the diet. Channel Island cattle are particularly prone to milk fever *away* from the Channel Islands, and the obvious explanation is the change from a soil heavily dressed with seaweed from which the cow derives the requirements of a highly efficient metabolism (this I think also explains the higher fat and solids content of milk in the Channel Islands) to

31. Natural treatment for cattle diseases. The garlic douche and enema should be given when an animal is fasting.

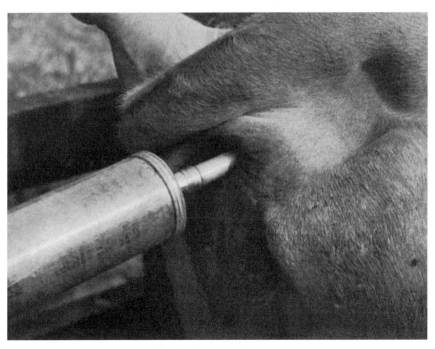

32. Giving a rectal enema.

33. The Jersey bull.

34. The Jersey cow.

soils which never get even as much as a smell of the sea, and in most cases precious little organic matter of *any* kind.

In addition to the use of seaweed wherever possible, organic manuring and the use of deep-rooting herbs in the pastures will contribute greatly to improved metabolism and the prevention of milk fever.

Treatment

Having fed the cow to the point of milk fever, or having bought one just after someone else has 'steamed-up' it, and she goes down with milk fever, it is too late to be certain that seaweed powder will act quickly enough, though there is no doubt it will help. So milk out the udder and inflate it with the apparatus which you should have had in readiness beforehand, and which is available from veterinary equipment suppliers.

The equipment consists of a teat syphon and filter chamber which filters the air which is blown through it into each quarter through the teat, after the udder has been thoroughly washed and milked out. The effect of this inflation of the udder is to prevent any further flow of milk into the udder and stop the drain of hormones and minerals from the blood stream to the udder. This enables the cow's system to adjust itself slowly to the demands which heavy milk production are putting upon it. The cow should also have a dose of two tablespoonfuls of seaweed powder in molasses and warm water (two tablespoonfuls of molasses) every three hours until she is up and walking about again. Into this mixture should be added four leaf-plasma tablets each time, to supply the vital tonic elements of grasses and herbs without the protein stimulant.

It is essential that the cow is kept propped up in the normal sitting position with bales of straw. On no account allow her to stretch out on her side. Then, if she appears slowly to be improving don't rush her to get up. She may, and quite understandably too, need a few hours' rest.

GRASS TETANY

Grass tetany is a more recent and more acute form of milk fever, and though it has been given a new name it has all the same symptoms and causes as milk fever, i.e. over-stimulation of milk secretion by the excessive protein of a rich clover ley, especially on top of the use of high protein cattle cake. But because it is far quicker in its action and results in death often before there has been an opportunity to treat the cow, it has been regarded as a separate disease. It may, however, be prevented in exactly the same way as I have advised for milk fever, and the treatment is the same should you be fortunate enough to catch the cow while she is still alive.

RED-WATER OR MURRAIN

Red-water is the result of tick infestation, especially on marshy land. The best prevention is to plough and reseed following a dressing of three tons to the acre of ground limestone. Where this is not practicable, tick attacks on cows may be kept to the minimum by grazing sheep on the same land. The tick prefers sheep which are themselves immune from the poison resulting from the tick bites.

Treatment

Follow exactly the same treatment as for Husk or Hoose, but with double the first dose of garlic and the addition of a dose of 2 lb. of common salt at the outset given in a treebarks powder gruel (two dessertspoonfuls of treebark blend, two dessertspoonfuls of molasses and warm water). After two hours give 2 pints of linseed oil with 2 oz. of turpentine. Continue 8 garlic tablets daily and don't press the animal to take food too soon.

RHEUMATISM

All food is withheld from the animal, and a fast continued for a week, or until the lameness has disappeared—whichever is the shorter. During the fast nothing whatever is given, except water, and the animal is confined in a house without straw bedding. Sawdust, peat moss or old sacks are used for bedding. Rectal enemas are given daily during the fast, using a bucketful of warm water each time. Garlic is given morning and night at the rate of 4 tablets or 2 whole plants.

The playing of cold water on to the affected part, for ten minutes morning and night, during the treatment will help to speed the cure by stimulating the blood circulation at the point of toxic accumulation, thereby assisting the process of purification.

At the end of the fast the animal is introduced gradually to compost-grown green food only, for a week, unless the lameness appears by that time to be cured, in which case a little hay is also introduced. Thereafter, gradually bring the cow back on to her normal diet, having regard to the fact that the feeding of manufactured concentrates is particularly to be avoided. The best production ration is made up of three parts (by weight) of ground oats to one part linseed. All cereals, as with green food, organically grown; it is advisable always when feeding sick animals, to choose foods grown on soil which has received good dressings of properly made compost.

Should the condition not be completely cured by one treatment, or in the event of it recurring at a later date, repeat this treatment periodically until the animal is completely healthy, ensuring in the intervals between treatments that the animal has an adequate supply of organically grown bulky food. Feeding which includes a wide variety of herbs, especially parsley and celery which have special properties in the prevention and treatment of rheumatism. Dried powdered parsley and celery may also be given during the fasting treatment by placing one dessertspoonful of each (preferably at different times) on the back of the animal's tongue—or in water as a drench. The regular use of garlic in some form is essential if there is any tendency to rheumatism or any catarrhal condition.

RINGWORM, ECZEMA, MANGE, AND OTHER SKIN DISEASES

I have grouped skin troubles, whether parasitic or merely the result of systemic elimination, because the treatment is almost identical. All skin troubles arise from deficiency feeding initially and may be tackled by a combination of fasting, improved nutrition, and external herbal treatment.

With any skin trouble fast the animal first of all for two days, unless it is very young when one day fast and one day on light milk or green food diet will suffice, and give a gentle laxative—either the liquid from 12 senna pods soaked in a pint of water, or 8 rhubarb tablets each night for three nights.

Then put the animal on to a diet of green food only—whatever quantity is normal for the age of the animal. With ringworm dress the parts with veterinary iodine initially and then follow with daily dressing of a herbal healing cream which I have evolved from the most effective cleansing and healing herbs, garlic, marshmallow, comfrey and chickweed. It is not easy to make up your own cream but I have arranged for my formula, together with the blended herbs which are suggested in other treatments, to be made generally available from reliable sources.

For skin troubles other than ringworm, fasting and a change to entirely green food diet as advised above, but no iodine should be used. The affected parts should be bathed in warm water, then daily dressed with the herbal healing cream, until the trouble has nearly subsided when it should be allowed to dry up and be left without further attention. Fresh air and sunshine should be allowed to the maximum available.

It is most important that the bulk of the diet should consist of fresh whole, and as far as possible green, food in order to maintain a healthy skin.

TEAT SORES OR COWPOX

Cows often develop sore teats during milking, particularly if their udders are being washed regularly with disinfectant. Cowpox is also a troublesome complaint which tends to spread if not stopped.

Prevention

Give up the use of disinfectant, for it will not prevent mastitis (see my explanation of the real causes of mastitis under that heading in this book) and then proceed to apply the following healing treatment.

Treatment

Wash the wound in warm water and salt, and dry thoroughly. Dress the wound or sore with the herbal healing cream advised for skin troubles, then wrap the sore with waterproof adhesive tape (which may be obtained at any chemist's shop). Don't disturb the bandage until a clean piece of tape appears to be needed when the sore may again be dabbed clean with a dry cloth dressed with the healing cream and wrapped with adhesive tape again. Always see that the tape completely covers the sore during milking for the less the place is disturbed or rubbed once it has been dressed, and the longer it can be kept dry (except for the healing cream) the quicker it will clear up.

STERILITY

The real causes of sterility start at birth when both cow and calf are deprived of the natural stimulus essential to the health of the reproductive organs, which suckling provides.

Prevention

Rear all calves naturally on foster mothers or their own dams (one quarter or less for calf—the rest for you) and give abundance of natural mineral-rich food throughout the productive life. Avoid over-exploitation.

Treatment

To commence the treatment, the affected animal is confined without food of any kind for a period of at least seven days—for the first and second days also deprive it of water. If it appears to be in good condition at the end of seven days, the fast is extended for a further meek, allowing a limited amount of water, i.e. about one bucketful worning and night. Rectal enemas and vaginal douches are given once daily during the fast, using at least four gallons of water each time, for each enema, rectal and vaginal. It is preferable to continue the enema each time until the water discharged is clear. Into the last half-gallon of water each time dissolve four crushed garlic tablets and if possible retain in the intestine and uterus respectively, as long as the cow will naturally hold the water.

Give a dose of garlic, the whole of two chopped garlic plants, twice daily, or 6 tablets of prepared garlic morning and night during the fast. This is given in a drench of the liquid from a bucketful of raspberry leaves or 2 to 3 oz. of dried, cut raspberry leaves, soaked or boiled in hot water. The garlic helps to eliminate the toxins which cause sterility and the raspberry leaf tea has a powerful tonic effect on the uterus and organs of reproduction.

When the fast is ended the animal is reintroduced to compost-grown green food only, such as oats and vetches, kale, or any other composted green crop available, or failing this, to controlled grazing of pasture which have received a dressing of compost during the last two years. A small field, with not too much growth, is suitable for this, and if the growth is not too lush the cattle may be turned on to it continuously.

The animal is continued on compost-grown green food only, for a period of five weeks, then reintroducing organically grown cereals. Linseed—

mixed in the proportions of one part of linseed to two parts of coarsely ground organically grown wheat, the richest source of vitamin E, the anti-sterility vitamin, is helpful as well as the green food, up to a maximum of 3 lb. per animal, morning and night. After a few days of this diet the animal is returned gradually to a production ration of 4 lb. per gallon of milk produced. The production ration should consist of one part ground linseed to three parts ground oats, with the addition when available of a little coarsely ground wheat or bran. One dessertspoonful of seaweed powder daily provides the best natural mineral supplement.

In severe cases this treatment will need to be repeated two or three times and the cow then turned out to run with a bull on a herbal ley and if possible a seaweed mineral ration should be provided in some form.

Sterility in the bull should be treated in exactly the same way, with the exception of course of the vaginal douche. The additional use of the herb, mint, especially wild mint if it can be found, or obtained from herbalists, in almost any quantity, will help to speed the cure.

VAGINITIS

Vaginitis is inflammation of the vagina, and is simply another manifestation of the condition which causes sterility or temporary infertility. Treatment should be the same as for sterility. Any kind of disinfectant douche or pessary, other than the non-irritant and natural cleanser garlic, should be rigorously avoided. Many temporarily infertile cows have been rendered permanently sterile by the use of strong disinfectant which merely irritates the delicate mucous membrane of the genital organs.

The common practice of inserting an antiseptic pessary after calving a cow, is itself often the cause of sterility. If the cow is allowed the stimulus of the suckling calf for at least four days or a week after calving the natural flow of hormones in the uterus and vagina will do all the cleansing that is necessary.

METRITIS

Metritis is a condition of inflammation in the uterus which may take either an acute or a chronic form.

The acute form of metritis is usually the result of a difficult calving or retention of a portion of the placenta or afterbirth. Another cause is the violent removal of the afterbirth causing slight injury to the wall of the uterus. Where this is internal injury effective treatment is difficult, especially if it has not been observed in time.

Freshly calved cows should be watched closely for ten days or a fortnight after calving, for any sign of swelling of the vulva, or unhealthy discharge. A healthy vulva is soft and pliant, and a clear pink in colour. Any hardening of the vulva or change in colour to a fiery red should be investigated at once. Discharges, which immediately after calving are quite to be expected, should be as clear as the white of an uncooked egg. White or yellow colouring in the discharge, or undue blood, call for a closer examination of the cause.

Acute Metritis Treatment

Though fasting always helps the healing of a wound, the length of the fast will depend on the condition of the animal. Acute metritis caught soon enough will not necessitate more than a day's, or two days' fasting, whereas when the condition has become chronic a longer fast is necessary to enable the system to dispose of the accumulated pus.

Green food only should be given when the fast is ended, or in winter some good hay may also be fed, but a light diet only is necessary. The system is always better able to carry through successful healing when the digestive process is either stopped completely or kept at a minimum.

Chronic metritis may be the result of an injury to the uterus during calving, which treatment has failed to cure, or acute metritis which has been left untreated, or, more commonly the cumulative effect of a long period of denatured feeding which has produced wastes in the region of the uterus which have, when the opportunity occurs, to be discharged. The opportunity for this discharge comes after calving when the uterus is empty. This results in yet another form of temporary sterility.

Treatment should be exactly as for sterility, see page 131.

INJURIES, CUTS AND WOUNDS

The most common injuries experienced by a cow are cut teats, broken horns, or torn skin.

In all cases of cuts, whether on the teat or other part of the body, the first need is to get it clean. There is nothing better for this than a weak solution of salt and warm water, followed by a rinse with cold water. I do not favour disinfectants of any kind. The wound will not turn septic if it is clean and the only way to get it clean is to use water, water and water. Every disinfectant of a chemical nature has the object of destroying bacteria, which are part of the healing process. It also has the effect of delaying the healing of an open wound by irritating the exposed nerve ending and depressing the blood plasma and hormone secretions which 'knit' the wound together. The only 'disinfectant' I know which does not have this delaying effect to the process of healing is garlic and even this should not be used, except initially.

If bleeding continues apply a cold water pack, renewing the cold water as often as possible. This is prepared by soaking a clean cloth in cold water, and folding it to form a pad rather larger than the wound, apply it by pressing it on to the wound by hand, repeating until bleeding stops. Then if it is possible to tie the pack on, leave it there for a few hours, recharging it with cold water as often as convenient until the wound appears to be closing. Then leave it to dry.

A cut teat may be treated in the same way as any other cut or wound, but if the cow is in milk it will be necessary to wrap it with waterproof adhesive bandage or tape. The wrapping should be kept as dry as possible and renewed as often as necessary to keep it clean. If the cut is so big as to prevent milking by hand or machine, a teat bougie (available from veterinary instrument suppliers) should be inserted to draw the milk. It is wise to keep a bougie in your veterinary chest in readiness.

If the horn is damaged but not completely broken away, it may be saved by a dressing of Stockholm tar, after washing in a solution of garlic and water, then bandaged in such a way as to hold it in position. If the outer shell of the horn comes away without breaking the core, protect the core with a bandage for a few days, then dress it with Stockholm tar and leave it to harden as it will.

Disease	Symptoms	Cause	Prevention	Treatment Sequence
Abortion (page 106)	Premature signs of imminent calving	Deficient diet or over-feeding. Catarrhal accumulations, discharging in uterus	Natural methods of management. Fast animal first signs, garlic and birth herbs, senna or rhubarb pill laxative	Give suckling calf. Then treat as sterility
Acetonaemia (page 110)	Sweet, sickly smell of breath—off food, list-less	High protein feeding and forcing milk yield	Low protein feeding, ample natural food. Minimum food just before and after calving	Immediate fasting; treebarks and molasses gruel. Leaf-plasma tablets, enemas daily during fast; then bran mashes, hay
Actinomycosis or Wooden Tongue (page 112)	Swelling and hardening of base of tongue or throat	Iodine deficiency	Regular use of seaweed powder in the diet—herbal leys	Fast; 1 pint molasses, 6 garlic tablets a.m. and p.m., 2 tablespoons sea weed powder twice daily
Bloat or Hoven (page 114)	Distention of first stomach	Fermentation set up by undigested foods in conjunction with clovers and grasses	Fast cows 12–24 hours before putting on lush grass. Give charcoal to absorb gases. Sow and use only herbal leys (see page 91)	In severe cases pierce stomach; 1 pint linseed oil; charcoal. Twisted rope of hay down throat; rubber tube in anus. Fast before further food
Calf Scour (page 116)	Diarrhoea	Excessive or dirty food; too much protein	Control milk to 5–6 lb. daily—direct from cow	Fast 24 hours; cold water and garlic; controlled suckling
Cow-pox (page 130)	See teat sores			
Eczema (page 129)	See skin diseases			

135

Disease	Symptoms	Cause	Prevention	Treatment Sequence
Grass Tetany (page 127)	As milk fever but more sudden	Acute form of milk fever	Low protein feeding—light diet 2 weeks before and after calving	As milk fever
Husk or Hoose (page 116)	Husky cough in late summer and autumn; usually young stock	Lung worms from wet grass	Graze young stock on young leys—bring in when wet, from late summer onwards	Fast for two days; heavy garlic dosage followed by generous dry feeding
Johne's Disease (page 118)	Insatiable appetite followed by severe scouring with bubbles in dung—then loss of appetite and wasting	Intestinal fermentation of undigested artificial foods. Unnatural rearing as a calf	Natural foods rich in minerals; herbal leys; periodic fasting where any artificial food is used. Natural suckling of calves	Fast, keep intestines free of food as long as possible; garlic, enemas daily—then powdered fenugreek and treebarks gruel
Joint—ill (page 120)	Thickening of a joint—abscess on navel	Toxic condition of calf's dam—iodine deficiency	Mineral rich natural diet for pregnant dam. Seaweed manuring and feeding	Fast on honey and warm water 1 or 2 days; 2 garlic tablets a.m. and p.m.; 4 rhubarb tablets or senna tea nightly; teaspoon seaweed powder, a.m. and p.m.
Mastitis (page 121)	Abnormal milk; inflammation of udder	Catarrhal condition due to overfeeding or deficient diet	Natural feeding, ample green food organically grown. No forcing	Fast, garlic, cold water packs on udder and hind quarters; enemas if fast prolonged
Milk Fever (page 123)	Paddling hind legs after calving—collapse and coma	Excessive stimulation of milk secretion, generally too high protein diet. Mineral deficiency	Mineral feeding from organic source—light diet 2 weeks before calving; fast 2 days before and 1 day after calving	Inflate udder—2 tablespoons seaweed powder in molasses three hourly; 4 leaf-plasma tablets 3 hourly. Keep cow sitting up
Mange (page 129)	See skin diseases			

Disease	Symptoms	Cause	Prevention	Treatment Sequence
Red-Water or Murrain (page 128)	Discoloured urine—off food	Tick bites	Re-seed pastures, with ground limestone dressing—sheep to graze with cattle	As husk, plus 2 lb. common salt and treebarks gruel; 2 pt. linseed oil and 2 oz. turpentine
Rheumatism (page 128)	Lameness. Sometimes swelling of joints	Unnatural feeding, causing accumulation of acids at joints	Natural diet of mainly fresh food. Regular use of garlic	Fast for 1 week or longer —4 garlic tablets a.m. and p.m. Rectal enemas daily—then organically grown green food
Ringworm (page 129)	Circular raised ring of dry, scabby flesh. Loss of hair	Parasite, in conjunction with malnutrition	Healthy diet; good nutrition; clean conditions	Iodine dressing, followed by herbal healing cream. Green food laxative
Skin diseases (page 129)	Scurfy, mange, loss of hair or dry skin	Deficient diet, dirty conditions or parasites. Excessive feeding also a cause	Good nutrition; clean conditions of housing	Wash and apply herbal healing cream. Green food laxative
Sterility (page 131)	Failure to breed	Unnatural diet, excessive milk production, catarrhal accumulations. Nature's demand for a rest	Mineral rich organically grown fresh food. Avoid excessive feeding or too frequent calving. Allow calf to suckle dam for at least a week	Fast for 1–2 weeks: Rectal and vaginal enemas; 6 garlic tablets a.m. and p.m.—birth herbs —green food only for 5 weeks. Run with bull
Vaginitis (page 132)	Vaginal discharge	Ditto	Ditto	Ditto
Metritis (page 132)	Vaginal discharge	Ditto or injury	Ditto	Ditto
Teat Sores (page 130)	Scabs and sores on teats	Damage during milking —cuts. Disinfectants in washing water	Care in milking; use no disinfectants	Herbal healing cream— wrap sore with waterproof adhesive tape— keep dry after dressing
Worms (page 133)	See Husk or Hoose			

137

GESTATION PERIODS OF VARIOUS ANIMALS

Ass: $12\frac{1}{2}$ months, 380 days.
Mare : 11 months, 340 days.
Cow: $9\frac{1}{2}$ months, 40 to 41 weeks, or 281 to 285 days.
Ewe and Goat: 5 months, 20 to 21 weeks, or 140 to 147 days.
Sow: Less than 4 months, but over 16 weeks, 110 to 120 days.
Bitch: 9 weeks, 63 to 65 days.
Cat : 7 to 8 weeks, 50 to 56 days.
Hen sitting on eggs of the Hen: 21 days (19 to 24 days).
Hen sitting on eggs of the Duck : 30 days (28 to 32 days).
Duck sitting on eggs of Duck : 30 days (28 to 32 days).
Goose sitting on eggs of Goose : 30 days (28 to 33 days).
Turkey sitting on eggs of Turkey : 26 days (24 to 30 days).

OESTRUM (HEAT) PERIODS

	Duration of Oestrum	Return after Parturition	Return if not Impregnated
Mare	5–7 days	7–10 days	2–3 weeks or more
Cow	1 day	21–28 days	2–4 weeks or more
Ewe	1–2 days	4–6 months	17–20 days
Sow	2–4 days	5–6 weeks	20–21 days
Bitch	1–3 weeks	5–6 months	5–6 months

NORMAL PULSE, TEMPERATURE AND RESPIRATIONS

	Pulse beats per minute	Respirations per minute	Temperature degrees F.
Horse	38–43	8–12	100–101
Cow	50–60	12–16	101–102
Sheep	75–80	20–30	103–104
Pig	70–80	20–30	102–103
Dog	80–90	15–35	101–102

Chapter 13

HERBAL MEDICINE ON THE FARM
AND A CHALLENGE

Most farmers will, at least until they have tried my methods with their own cattle, regard herbalism as merely a good living for quacks, trading on silly women and men with unfounded worries about perfectly sound health; those who have seen its result in curing humans will believe its successes to be founded on faith healing. But there can be no possibility of faith healing with cattle, though they have a great deal more common sense about health and means of maintaining it than most human beings. If left to themselves they would hunt up the very herbs I give them and they will naturally avoid other food until they are well.

Practically no labour is needed to provide the basic herbal requirements. Garlic is the most important and the only one needed in any quantity.

Garlic is one of the easiest plants to cultivate on the farm. On many farms it grows wild as Ramsons (*Allium ursinum*) and this wild garlic is the most valuable source of sulphur and other purifying agents. (The garden variety [*Allium sativum*] will do, though it is not as potent as the wild garlic.) It has the ability to disperse catarrhal mucus, the basis of most diseases. So that if there is anything which might approach qualification for the title 'cure-all' it is garlic. It is as near a cure-all as we are ever likely to get. All livestock farms would therefore benefit from the planting of a supply. Wild garlic may be transplanted like shallots, or sown from seed. Or, in these days of the deplorable and overworked expression 'no time', as an alternative, at least, until garlic is growing on the farm I have arranged for herbalists to make up tablets of the whole wild garlic plant dried and compressed, so that supplies may be kept in a convenient form always ready for us. When adequate supplies are growing they may be lifted and stored as with onions or shallots.

Garlic taints the milk *only* when taken in large quantities. A little occasionally, which is the way the cow would take it under natural conditions, will not taint the milk. The amount needed for treatment will not affect the milk.

Raspberry leaves may be gathered from the garden or the canes planted in the hedgerows. Any variety will do, wild or domestic. Blackberry leaf, though not as good, has similar properties.

All the other requirements I have advised are now available from veterinary herbalists. The cost is, in the long run, less than orthodox drugs or proprietary veterinary medicines, they may be kept in readiness for an indefinite period, and what makes them far better value for money than most orthodox drugs is that *they work*, if they are used as prescribed in this book, and they effect permanent cures not merely temporary suppression.

The modern farmer is prepared to risk his valuable stock on the word of the manufacturing chemist, the veterinary surgeon, and the research station. I am not asking him to risk even the farm cat without supporting evidence. Every treatment in this book I have used for many years on my own beasts. Moreover I have bought in cattle, given up after orthodox treatment has failed, cured them, and got profitable production from them, instead of paying the vet. to tell me that they were hopeless cases.

The following table lists *some* typical cases of disease treated entirely by herbal means, mainly of animals acquired for little or nothing as incurable. For obvious reasons it is only a brief selection covering the main diseases. There are now hundreds more on other farms as well as mine, which owe their survival to the herbal treatments described in this book.

Similarly the letters which follow in Appendix I are but a selection from the many farmers who have themselves successfully tried my methods.

Disease	Cow's name and number	Date and Condition when acquired, and how	Previous Owner	Date Cured	Subsequent Performance, etc.
Sterility and Mastitis	Canonteign Variety 44482	Purchased 30th June 1945. £20	Mrs. Hinchcliff-Bond, Cullompton, Devon	July 1945	Subsequently fell in ditch
Trichominiasis	Top Sergente 22274	Condemned by C. E. S. Scott, M.R.C.V.S., June 1943	W. B. Tobey, Aylesbury	November 1943	Still in use in herd at 11 years old
Sterility. No calf for 2 years	Aldermaston Mermaid 43968	Purchased "sterile" 30th June 1945. £14	Mrs. Hinchcliff-Bond, Cullompton, Devon	Calved 24th November 1946 and regularly	Gave 6701 lb., now owned by J. W. Reid of Launceston
Sterility	Everdon Double Daydream 44966	Purchased November 1947. £10	Mrs. D. Carter-Williams, Cheltenham	Calved 9th March 1948	Sold in calf to a dealer
Sterility. No calf or 2 years	Ramsden Fairycup 38317	Given to me 1947	Mrs. O. M. Osborn, St. Frances Farm, Ewshott, Dorset	Calved 18 September 1948	Gave 10,433 lb. 363 days. Died of old age
Mastitis, one quarter	Shipton Springsong 34641	Yeovil Market, 1945	Mr. E. J. Chave, Newton St. Loe, Bristol	1945	Sold to J. Blew of Highbridge
Mastitis	Brookside Dairymaid 8th	Yeovil Market 12th June 1946	Lady Hussey	1946	Used as foster mother. Died at 16
Mastitis, two quarters	Ovaltine Wizards Sultana 34330	Ovaltine Sale, August 1945	A. Wander Ltd., Abbots Langley	August 1945	Still calving annually at 16, and sound in all quarters

141

Disease	Cow's name and number	Date and Condition when acquired and how	Previous Owner	Date Cured	Subsequent Performance, etc.
Magnesium Deficiency	Winkle	1944 as heifer. Later collapsed with Magnesium Deficiency	Mr. D. M. Farrar, Bedford	1945. Calved 9th March 1946	Gave 900 galls. Bred several good heifers. Sold as non-pedigree
Johne's Disease	Popin Lass 71170	Yeovil Market, 1946	Imported by dealer	1946	Gave 9782 lb. 363 days. Still in herd
Summer Mastitis	Annabelle 3rd	Affected 20th August 1948 when she had given 7,600 lb.		29th August 1948	Went on to 9,735 lb. in 364 days. Sold to Mrs. J. V. Clarke, Wadhurst
Habitual Milk Fever	Millside Treasure 56332	October 1949	N. S. Inch of St. Austell	October 1951	Still in herd
Vibrio Foetus and resultant sterility	Julia's Waranee	Purchased May, 1951. £15	Mrs. Osborn, Rownhams Farm West Kington, Wiltshire	January 1952	Still in herd
Sterility	Knowle Marigold 79335	Sent to me for treatment February 1949 after A.I. vets. had failed for 12 months	Maj. Carleton-Cowper, Ash House, Winkleigh, Devon	Effectively served 4th July 1949	Calved successfully to date
Sterility and T.B. reactor	La Porte Karena 72108	Sent to me for treatment March 1949. Failed tuberculin test, April 1949	Maj. G. C. Phillips & A. S. Moore, Easton Farm, Bigbury, Devon	Effectively served 19th May 1949. Pass T.T., August 1949	Returned to owner. Subsequently calved Winkledown Electra 107023 on 23rd February 1950. Cow sold at Reading (Dispersal Sale) for 330 guineas, her calf for 100 guineas

HERBAL MEDICINE ON THE FARM—A CHALLENGE

The following criticism, which I received from a Dorset M.R.C.V.S., after the publication of my book, *Fertility Farming*, is no doubt typical of the orthodox veterinary attitude to my experiences with animal diseases. Whilst such sceptical comments are to be expected after so many generations of the germ and drug theory it is well that they should, for the sake of enlightenment, not go unanswered. I follow the veterinary surgeon's criticism with my reply and a challenge.

'I have read with considerable interest, but more misgiving, your book, *Fertility Farming*,' [he writes], 'I am not qualified to comment on the chapters concerned directly with crop-growing, but feel myself morally obliged to criticize some of the more outrageous and blatant errors in the chapters on animal disease, where your lack of knowledge is only surpassed by your illogical deductions. I will therefore proceed to take a few of your statements—I have only time to take a few—and put forward my own arguments, which are, I hope, somewhat more reasonable.

'Disease not caused by bacteria. A cow in sound health does not succumb to disease.'

If disease is not caused by bacteria can you tell me why injection of a guinea-pig with a *pure* culture of the organism of bovine T.B. invariably produces typical disease followed by death?

Injection of foot and mouth virus causes 100 per cent infection of the bovine animal.

B. Anthracis injection into the blood stream of cattle will produce typical symptoms of anthrax.

The only certain positive diagnosis of swine fever is to produce infection by injection of infected material from a suspected case in another pig.

Swine fever and foot-and-mouth are virus diseases, not bacterial, but the principal cause of disease in these cases is the causal organism, not the condition of the animal. Hundreds of other examples could easily be found.

'Bacteria arise as result of disease.'

This remarkable statement presupposes spontaneous generation which has been disproved many times beginning with a certain M. Pasteur, of whom you have perhaps heard.

'Summer mastitis, a natural cleansing process.'

Here you even write about one condition when you mean another. 'Summer mastitis' is an acute abscess of the udder occurring mainly on dry cows and heifers, resulting almost invariably in the loss of the affected quarter(s).

'Cold water stimulates quick exchange of blood.'

Cold water causes a physiological reflex contraction of peripheral blood vessels, thereby *inhibiting* a quick exchange of blood!

'Penicillin treatment suppresses catarrhal discharge.'

How an antibiotic agent acting only as a bacteriostatic is capable of suppressing discharge I am unable to explain, but extensive tests, scientifically carried out on hundreds of thousands of cattle, not a few score as on your farm, have proved beyond doubt that penicillin is a sure and permanent cure for the commoner forms of mastitis, not forgetting the possibility of infection at a future date.

Tuberculosis treatment—you mention only one case of a reactor becoming a non-reactor. This is by no means an uncommon occurrence, independent of any so-called treatment, and has a quite logical explanation. The lesion becomes inactive, a wall of connective tissue being framed around it, and antibodies are no longer found in the blood stream, hence no reaction can occur. It must not be forgotten that live bacilli are still present in this lesion, and any strain on the animal's system, calving, a chill, etc., may provoke a break-down of the original lesion, liberation of the organism into the blood stream, rapidly followed by emaciation and death, with the grave possibility of infecting other members of the herd.

I can only conclude that any 'results' you have obtained, based on so many scientifically incorrect surmises, must be ignored. You cry very loudly against modern drug treatment but I feel sure that if one of your own family was attacked by meningitis, or osteomyelitis—two diseases quite independent of bodily health, you would be the first to agree to penicillin treatment, and would not be content to fast them and treat them with garlic tablets. How strange that there is any disease at all in the garlic-eating countries in the world!

I look forward with keen enjoyment to receiving your reply.'

My reply was as follows:

You instance the injection of 'pure cultures' resulting in disease as an argument in favour of the old germ theory. The injection of any foreign matter into the system, especially directly into the blood stream, is likely to cause illness and possibly death. Ordinary human vaccination is a case in point. In the sixteen years ended December 1948, 2 children (under 5) died of smallpox but 72 died of vaccination (see replies to questions by Minister of Health between July 1938 and April 1949). In any case most humans and animals are in a condition which calls for the cleansing action of bacteria and if this pre-condition of the ultimate symptom (which you call disease) is exaggerated by a continuation of the feeding and living which caused it, the bacteria are unequal to the task. The only reasonable way to allow the bacteria to complete satisfactorily the task of healing, with which nature has charged them, is to stop all additions to the system in the form of food—especially unnatural food, which only adds to the toxic accumulations.

I was not aware that Pasteur proved anything except there is a lot of money to be made by chemical and drug manufacturers out of the almost criminal, and certainly blasphemous, theory that nature provided bacteria as a curse and not a blessing to human and animal kind. I prefer to agree with Pasteur's contemporary, Béchamp.

As I have cured many cases of summer mastitis and accepted the challenge of a Ministry vet. to treat an early case under Ministry supervision (not yet taken up—perhaps you would like to do something practical about this instead of theoretical argument) I can only disagree emphatically with your remarks about this disease.

My statement about cold water does not deny your own explanation of the action of cold water on the blood vessels. You will find if you observe your own reactions, when you take your cold bath in the morning, that the cold water drives the blood from the surface of the skin (peripheral blood vessels if you like), creating a kind of vacuum which must quickly result in a return rush of fresh, pure blood, giving the well-known (though I fear now rarely experienced by most people) feeling of tingling warmth and well-being, and pink blush of colour which the quick exchange of blood has caused.

Penicillin suppresses catarrhal discharge by halting a natural process of bacterial combustion and dispersal. The use of penicillin is like treating a nuisance at the old town garbage dump by killing the garbage man who is collecting and dumping it there.

The hundreds of thousands of tests you mention are invalidated by the fact that they all worked on the assumption that the symptom was the disease, and in every case a cure was recorded as soon as superficial symptoms of the disease were no longer evident. I have followed *some* of the thousands of penicillin 'cured' mastitis cases, to cure effectively and permanently, without drugs, the trouble which has resulted, when the cow owner in question has lost patience with repeated failures of penicillin to bring a *lasting* cure. Not all veterinary surgeons are as dogmatic as you about the ability of penicillin to effect 'sure and permanent cure' for the commoner forms of mastitis. Have you not heard of the 'penicillin resistance' which is now the explanation of many penicillin failures?

What I am claiming is a 'sure and permanent cure' for *all* forms of mastitis, and one which is within the ability of every farmer to achieve himself without chemical drugs. I challenge you or anyone else to disprove my claim under whatever supervision you care to arrange. Have the courage of your criticisms and allow me to treat a case of mastitis, strep, staph., summer, or whatever variety you care to take, provided treatment can be started within forty-eight hours of clinical evidence of abnormality. Alternatively, arrange official tests of my treatments under my supervision. [See also following letters on Foot and Mouth Disease.]

It is wrong that simple cures should be dismissed without investigation, while untold damage is done to the cattle and food supply of this country through the failure of one wonder drug after another.

I have made no claims to cure tuberculosis, though I know that early cases can be cured. To 'cure' a reactor can no more constitute a cure of tuberculosis than the official tuberculosis test constitutes a diagnosis of tuberculosis. Not until the official test is an *infallible* means of diagnosing tuberculosis shall we be able to say that the 'cure' of a reactor constitutes a cure of tuberculosis.

In the meantime old Top Sergente (and other ex-reactors) show no signs of impending emaciation—though he is in his eleventh year and has apparently been harbouring those lesions full of live bacteria for nearly seven years. Only stork-headed fear of the impending end to the quackery of the drug racket can make you say that my results must be ignored because they are based on scientifically incorrect surmises. The fact is my treatments *work*, which is all that interests the farmer, and livestock breeder. The farmer is becoming increasingly suspicious of the 'results' which are tied to the sale of drugs or chemical fertilizers. He is beginning to tire of the endless procession of wonder drugs chasing the lengthening lines of new diseases.

Your premise that meningitis and osteomyelitis are both independent of bodily health is so ridiculously wrong that I hardly need answer it. But in the very unlikely event of a properly fed and healthy child of mine getting either, I should certainly not allow the injection of drugs, which would only add to the task of natural healing of which the system is itself capable if not unduly burdened.

Why it should be strange that there should be disease in the garlic-eating countries I can't imagine. I have never heard it suggested that garlic is proof against all the commercial food partialisers and adulterators, let alone the array of chemical and drug injectors, almost as vast and wealthy in the garlic-eating countries as anywhere else.

I certainly would never suggest that eating garlic is an antidote to agenized, emasculated bread and macaroni, polished rice and white sugar, Coco-cola and tobacco, vaccination and the whole bag of tricks in the chemist's shop. But it will *help* a lot and in treatment, used to the exclusion of all these killers of commercialized human and animal 'welfare', it will *cure* a lot.

I had not intended dealing at such length with your comments, for as you may imagine my correspondence is beyond human ability to satisfy 100 per cent, and many letters have to be ignored. I had left yours in the hope of arranging a personal meeting to discuss your obviously searching questions for it is the only effective way. I still hope, should you continue to dispute my work, that we may talk rather than write and that you will remain sufficiently open-minded to try some of my treatments as willingly as you buy the ready-made treatments of the druggists.

I sense from your letter, and the fact that you have taken the trouble to write to me, that you are not so hidebound as to close your eyes to results which I will show you, and not so dull as to imagine that nature would fail without the manufacturing chemist.

In addition to the previous correspondence, I have urged in any personal contacts with our local Ministry veterinary officer, a proper investigation of my claims for natural immunity and the simple cures which I have developed for the common cattle diseases.

Several letters to the press on a similar topic failed to achieve publication. A letter to the secretary of the Animal Health Trust (which is raising huge sums of money, mainly from farmers, for research into animal diseases) enclosing my book, *Cure Your Own Cattle*, and offering to demonstrate under proper controls the effectiveness and simplicity of my treatments, and the means and value of building natural immunity, was ignored.

It was *The Times*, and shortly after *Everybody's Weekly*, which eventually had the courage to make public my challenge to the Ministry and veterinary profession to investigate my claims.

The following letters appeared:

HERBAL MEDICINE ON THE FARM—A CHALLENGE

The Times, 24th December 1951

The review of foot and mouth disease by Dr. Wooldridge ignores the possibility of the development of natural immunity in our cattle. This is surely the only intelligent approach to all disease. There are already the classic examples of the complete immunity, when placed in physical contact with animals suffering from foot-and-mouth disease, of animals which have been reared and fed naturally on food from organically manured soil, reported by Sir Albert Howard and the Marquis Stanga. More recently I have demonstrated that animals reared and fed exclusively on organically grown food can be given permanent immunity to Johne's disease and other so-called virus transmitted diseases; also that animals sufering from sterility and mastitis may quickly and cheaply be cured by simple herbal adjustments and a régime of organically grown food.

The official slaughter policy denies the opportunity of similar experiments with foot-and-mouth disease, but I am prepared to demonstrate under proper controls and supervision that foot and mouth disease as well as the other more common diseases of cattle are not transmittable in normal circumstances to animals which are naturally reared on organically manured soils.

Disease is becoming such a serious menace to our food supplies that it would be nothing less than criminal for the Ministry of Agriculture and the Animal Health Trust to continue to ignore such facts.

Everybody's Weekly, 1st March 1952.

Should we slaughter the Minister of Agriculture and his staff when they get influenza, which is the equivalent in humans of foot-and-mouth disease? The article by your Farming Correspondent in December says nothing about the development of *natural* immunity, shown by Sir Albert Howard and the Marquis Stanga to be completely effective with animals reared naturally and fed on food grown in fertile organically manured soil.

The commonsense approach, if only the powerful vested interests in disease can be overcome, is to rear and manage cattle so that they don't get it. Animals naturally bred and reared, and organically fed, *do not get disease;* and I have cured other farmers' 'incurable' rejects of the two common scourges, sterility and mastitis, by simple herbal adjustments and an adequate natural diet.

The slaughter policy of the Ministry of Agriculture does not allow me to demonstrate the effectiveness of such methods with foot-and-mouth disease. *But I am prepared to demonstrate under official supervision that animals so managed do not get foot-and-mouth disease, even when living with animals suffering from the disease.*

In reply to my letter, Dr. W. R. Wooldridge wrote the following letter which was published in *The Times* on 31st December 1951.

Mr. Newman Turner again advances the claims of a natural immunity alleged to follow the feeding and rearing of animals on foodstuffs from organically manured soil. Many scientists, including some within the Ministry of Agriculture and in the Animal Health Trust, are working upon the inter-relationship of food and resistance to disease, and it may be that rigid scientific evidence may one day support in part claims made by Mr. Newman Turner and his colleagues. At present, however, their claims are not substantiated. The outbreaks of foot-and-mouth disease do not show any marked discrimination in favour of either poorly fed livestock or those nurtured on farms where the largest quantities of artificial fertilizers are used. Furthermore, one might mention that disease was rampant among animals long before artificial fertilizers were widely used, as may be instanced by the outbreak of cattle plague in Great Britain in 1865, when 233,699 cattle died.

Yours faithfully,
W. R. WOOLDRIDGE,
Chairman of Council and Scientific Director, Animal Health Trust, 232-5 Abbey House, Victoria Street, London, S. W.I. 28th December.

It is encouraging to know from Dr. Wooldridge that work is at last being done on lines at least approaching those I have tried to pioneer on the farm. So far, my own practical experience has not been called on. But there is no secret about my methods of disease prevention and treatment. Every successful treatment has been published and is available in my writings for any farmer to try himself on his own farm, and for official investigators to investigate.

The immense losses from animal disease on the farm, and the colossal expenditure of taxpayers' money on research into costly orthodox drug therapy demand that my simple treatments should be given an official test. I am ready for the sake of animal health and the pockets of my fellow farmers to demonstrate the ease, and infinitesimal cost at which our common cattle diseases can be cured, and in the future prevented.

In the next chapter I have tried to make the case for an experiment into natural immunity to Foot and Mouth Disease and offered some of my own cattle for the purpose.

Chapter 14

FOOT-AND-MOUTH DISEASE
Can be Prevented Without Slaughter

No one, not even its most ardent advocate, would consider the official policy of wholesale slaughter of foot-and-mouth-diseased cattle an ideal means of combatting the disease. I believe it to be a policy of utter despair. The destruction of all cattle immediately they are found to be suffering from foot and mouth disease, was made compulsory in an effort to eliminate the disease from Britain, or at least to reduce the number of outbreaks. Far from having achieved this purpose it has had no effect on the number of animals slaughtered. Foot-and-mouth disease is as prevalent in Britain to-day as ever it was. In the six months November 1951 to May 1952, nearly 400 herds were slaughtered.

My experience of dealing with animal disease makes me feel quite sure that this increase will continue in spite of the slaughter policy. Until it is recognized that the only defence against *all* disease is the development of *natural* immunity neither poleaxe nor hypodermic needle will help towards a solution. Health is not something which can be bought from the manufacturing chemist. It is the inevitable consequence of the natural life. Disease is not a devil that can be exorcised by magic potions or prevented by slaughter. It is the inevitable outcome of man's perversion of natural law.

So serious are the dangers of foot-and-mouth disease to the future of the British livestock industry and the food of the nation that it is time Ministry of Agriculture officials took a more realistic attitude to the whole problem, shook themselves free of the shot-in-the-arm theory and took a look at nature.

Is there any evidence of a possible answer to foot-and-mouth disease in nature? The disease is merely a bovine form of common influenza. If nothing at all is done for the cattle that get it, except to leave them alone, they recover in a few weeks. It has never been considered necessary to slaughter the Minister of Agriculture when he gets influenza, in order to save his staff. They who get it generally recover in spite of their unnatural lives. Cattle, too, will recover from foot and mouth disease far more easily than man recovers from the common cold provided they are given a natural chance.

But there is no need to consider the question of curing the disease. It need never be.

I have demonstrated that animals reared and fed exclusively on organically grown food can be given permanent immunity to Johne's disease and other so-called virus transmitted diseases; also that animals suffering from sterility and mastitis may quickly and cheaply be cured by simple herbal adjustments and a regime of organically grown food. Similarly, some work has already been done actually on foot-and-mouth disease which though by no means conclusive, or even scientific, gives at least some indication of the possibilities.

Sir Albert Howard writes, in *Farming and Gardening for Health or Disease,* of his experiences with foot-and-mouth disease in India:

'…I therefore put forward a request to have my own work cattle, so that my small farm of seventy-five acres could be a self-contained unit. I was anxious to select my own animals, to design their accommodation, and to arrange for their feeding, hygiene, and management. Then it would be possible to see: (1) what the effect of properly grown food would be on the well-fed working animal; and (2) how such livestock would react to infectious diseases. This request was refused several times on the ground that a research institute like Pusa should set an example of co-operative work rather than of individualistic effort. I retorted that agricultural advance had always been made by individuals rather than by groups and that the history of science proved conclusively that no progress had ever taken place without freedom. I did not get my oxen. But when I placed the matter before the Member of the Viceroy's Council in charge of agriculture (the late Sir Robert Carlyle, K.C.S.I.), I immediately secured his powerful support and was allowed to have charge of six pairs of oxen.

'I had little to learn in this matter, as I belong to an old agricultural family and was brought up on a farm which had made for itself a local reputation for the management of cattle. My animals were most carefully selected for the work they had to do and for the local climate. Everything was done to provide them with suitable housing and with fresh green fodder, silage and grain, all produced from fertile soil. They soon got into good fettle and began to be in demand at the neighbouring agricultural shows, not as competitors for prizes, but as examples of what an Indian ox should look like. The stage was then set for the project I had in view, namely, to watch the reaction of these well-chosen and well-fed oxen to diseases like rinderpest, septicaemia, and foot-and-mouth disease, which frequently devastated the countryside and sometimes attacked the large herds of cattle maintained on the Pusa Estate. I always felt that the real cause of such epidemics was either starvation, due to the intense pressure of the bovine population on the limited food supply, or, when food was adequate, to mistakes in feeding and management. The working ox must always have not only good fodder and forage, but ample time for chewing the cud, for rest, and for digestion. The grain ration is also important, as well as a little fresh green food—all produced by intensive methods of farming. Access to clean fresh water must also be provided. The coat of the working animal must also be kept clean and free from dung.

'The next step was to discourage the official veterinary surgeons, who often visited Pusa, from inoculating these animals with various vaccines and sera to ward off the common diseases. I achieved this by firmly refusing to have anything to do with such measures, at the same time asking these specialists to inspect my animals and to suggest measures to improve their feeding, management, and housing, so that my experiment could have the best possible chance of success. This carried the day. The veterinarians retired from the unequal contest and took no steps to compel me to adopt their remedies.

'My animals then had to be brought in contact with diseased stock. This was done by allowing them: (1) to use the common pastures at Pusa, on which diseased cattle sometimes grazed, and (2) to come in direct contact with foot-and-mouth disease. This latter was easy, as my small farmyard was only separated from one of the large cattle sheds of the Pusa Estate by a low hedge, over which the animals could rub noses. I have often seen this occur between my oxen and foot-and-mouth cases. Nothing happened. The healthy, well-fed animals reacted to this disease exactly as suitable varieties of crops, when properly grown, did to insect and fungus pests— no infection took place. Neither did any infection occur as the result of my oxen using the common pastures. This experiment was repeated year after year between 1910 and 1923, when I left Pusa for Indore. A somewhat similar experience was repeated at Quetta between the years 1910 and 1918, but here I had only three pairs of oxen. As at Pusa, the animals were carefully selected and great pains were taken to provide them with suitable housing, with protection from the intense cold of winter, and with the best possible food. Again no precautions were taken against disease and no infection took place.'

'...But this is not the whole of the foot-and-mouth story. When the 300 acres of land at Indore were taken over in the autumn of 1924, the area carried no fodder crops, so the feeding of forty oxen was at first very difficult. During the hot weather of 1925 these difficulties became acute. A great deal of heavy work was falling on the animals, whose food consisted of wheat straw, dried grass and millet stalks, with a small ration of crushed cotton seed. Such a ration might do for maintenance, but it was quite inadequate for heavy work. The animals soon lost condition and for the first and last time in my twenty-five years' Indore experience I had to deal with a few very mild cases of foot-and-mouth disease in the case of some dozen animals. The patients were rested for a fortnight and given better food, when the trouble disappeared never to return. But this warning stimulated everybody concerned to improve the hot-weather cattle ration and to secure a supply of properly made silage for 1926, by which time the oxen had recovered condition. From 1927 to 1931 these animals were often exhibited at agricultural shows as type specimens of what the local breed should be. They were also in great demand for the religious processions which took place in Indore city from time to time, a compliment which gave intense pleasure to the labour staff of the Institute.

'This experience, covering a period of twenty-six years at three widely separated centres—Pusa in Bihar and Orissa, Quetta on the Western Frontier, and Indore in Central India—convinced me that foot-and-mouth disease is a consequence of malnutrition pure and simple, and that the remedies which have been devised in countries like Great Britain to deal with the trouble, namely the slaughter of the affected animals, are both superficial and also inadmissible. Such attempts to control an outbreak should cease. Cases of foot-and-mouth disease should be utilized to tune up practice and to see to it that the animals are fed on the fresh produce of fertile soil. The trouble will then pass and will not spread to the surrounding areas, provided the animals there are also in good fettle. Foot-and-mouth outbreaks are a sure sign of bad farming.

'How can such preventive methods of dealing with diseases like foot-and-mouth be set in motion? Only by a drastic reorganization of present-day veterinary research. Instead of the elaborate and expensive laboratory investigations now in progress on this disease, which are not leading to any practical result, a simple preventive trial on the following lines should be started. An area of suitable land should first be got into first class condition by means of subsoiling, the reform of the manure heap, and reformed leys containing deep-rooting plants like lucerne, sainfoin, burnet, and chicory, and the various herbs needed to keep livestock in condition. The animals should be carefully selected to suit the local conditions and should first of all be got into first-class fettle by proper feeding and management. Everything will then be ready for a simple experiment in disease prevention. A few foot-and-mouth cases should be let loose among the herds, the reaction of both healthy and diseased animals being carefully watched. The diseased animals will soon recover. There will most likely be no infection of the healthy stock. At the worst there will only be the mildest possible attack which will disappear in a fortnight or so.'

'... Foot-and-mouth is considered to be a virus disease. It could perhaps be more correctly described as a simple consequence of malnutrition, due either to the fact that the proteins of the food have not been properly synthesized, or to some obvious error in management. One of the most likely aggravations of the trouble is certain to be traced to the use of artificial manures instead of good old-fashioned muck or compost.'

Extract from an experiment by the Marquis Stanga in 1938 at Cremona

'It is time to view from a new angle the problem created by the infections that so often ravage our herds. Up to now in Europe we have spent large sums for medicines and vaccines with very poor results, especially so if one considers the renewed outbreaks of these same diseases. The fact that the live vaccines endanger the health of the animal and that lymphs have little practical use whilst contagious abortion, vaginitis and foot and mouth continue unrestricted makes one feel it is time to say enough! Let us try something else. Looking back and remembering that over thirty years ago I started rearing pigs naturally in the open air, thus eliminating completely from my pens all the diseases of pigs, I thought that it might be possible to arrive at similar results with cattle. Naturally these ideas of mine had to be tried out by a series of experiments and I decided to go ahead.

'I chose a small uncovered yard and on the 17th October 1936 a Holstein bull calf was born in the open and was kept in the open air with no shelter whatsoever. Groups of control calves were also kept, some as are normally kept in Cremona, others in a semi open-air way. All the calves were fed the same way and the control groups were inoculated with serum and vaccines. It was found that the Martyr, as the experimental calf was named, required from the first days less food than the others although he showed more energy and vitality and more growth than the control calves. The Metereological Observatory of Cremona supplied details of the weather records:

'October. Varied with two days of fog and two clear days.
'November. Foggy. Four days of rain and the temperature below zero centograde.
'December. Foggy. Three days of snow. Nine days of continued rain.
'January. Ten days of snow. Many frosts. Three days clear. The rest foggy.
'February. Similar.

'The calf from a purely milk diet had passed on to solid food, but required much less food than the control calves. So much so, that I began to wonder if the fresh air and natural life facilitates the production of blood and a better assimilation of foods, whilst the animals kept under artificial conditions require more food to produce those anti-bodies so necessary for their life's fight. Although the calf had not been inoculated with the usual serums and vaccines he continued in good health, whilst several of the control calves died of pneumonia and all developed the usual cough and showed the yellowish viscid mucus at the nostrils that always afflicts my calves. The calf was permanently kept in the open air whilst we waited for foot-and-mouth to break out so as to prove if the natural existence would make the animal more or less immune. On the 6th February 1938, when the Martyr was over a year old he was taken to a farm at Basiglio where foot-and-mouth had broken out. The Martyr was kept in the farmyard until 7th March 1938, always, of course, in the open air and in contact with the farm employees. From here he was taken to another infected farm at S. Vito di Gaggiano where he not only lived amongst infected animals but was allowed to serve 10 infected cows who lived with him in his paddock at the height of the infection. He remained here until 8th April 1938 and was then taken to a farm at Chiaravalle, also infected with foot-and-mouth where the experiment was carried a step further, and on the 9th and 10th April the lips and tongue of the bull were smeared with saliva taken from infected animals. After all this he did not contract the disease and he returned home on the 17th May 1938 in perfect health.'

The official slaughter policy at present denies the opportunity of similar experiments in this country. But the combination of my own successes with other diseases and the reports quoted from Sir Albert Howard and the Marquis Stanga are surely enough to warrant the commencement of similar official experiments to decide once and for ever whether it is really possible in this country to rear animals economically in such a way as to give them natural immunity to foot-and-mouth disease.

I would willingly provide from my own herd some cattle of third generation naturally-bred and organically-reared, for an experiment of this kind, if the Ministry of Agriculture would allow me to supervise their feeding and management throughout the experiment.

Will the Ministry continue to ignore such a proposal which can cost the nation but a minute fraction of the present research into animal diseases, and *may* produce an answer to one of the greatest agricultural problems of all time? There is nothing—not even face—to lose, except in refusing my offer.

APPENDIXES

Appendix 1

LETTERS FROM SUCCESSFUL USERS OF MY VETERINARY METHODS

It may seem strange for a farmer to print 'testimonials', as though he were a patent medicine manufacturer, but because of the unusual nature of my methods of treatment, I quote a series of entirely unsolicited letters as examples of the way my methods have succeeded for others. Unlike a manufacturer selling a pennyworth of chemicals with threepenny worth of bottle and several shillings' worth of stamp duty, purchase tax, advertising and profit, I can have no financial interest in people feeding or growing their own wild garlic. These cases are selected from many, to show the diseases with which others have succeeded and that the success of my herbal methods does not depend on my eye for judging curable cattle, my soil, climate, or even any special skill or magic touch with which I may have been blessed.

MAJOR J. A. R. WISE, Trevarren Farm, St. Columb, Cornwall:

I have cured two cases of mastitis with the greatest of ease by your methods; and one cow who has repeatedly returned to service, held the first time after undergoing five days of your treatment. Since giving up feeding cake the vaginitis trouble in my herd has disappeared.

MR. A. J. HOLLINHURST, Barns Fold Farm, Goosnargh, Preston, Lancs.:

I write to tell you of our success with your treatment. Our first success was with navel ill. The calf at birth seemed to be quite normal but after a few days began to look a bit seedy, hair standing up, and stiff movements. We thought the stiffness may have been hereditary as her dam is a rheumaticky sort of animal, though quite old, perhaps about 14 years.

On feeling at the navel it was slightly swollen and wet with a mattery sort of discharge. We informed the vet., and he came and examined the navel, and regarded it as a bad case of navel ill. He prescribed hot-water fomentations and M. & B.s. We carried out his instructions but the discharge continued although not as severe, and then it seemed to heal although still rather swollen.

After another day or so we noticed an inclination of the calf to frequent urination, but found it was not water but matter. We informed the vet. and he came again and left a further dose of M. & B.s, but said that it was no good really as the bladder and kidneys must be in a bad way, and suggested getting rid of the unfortunate animal.

By this time we had in our possession your book, *Cure Your Own Cattle* and decided to give your methods a trial. We had decided to do so earlier than this but were waiting for delivery of garlic tablets and seaweed powder. But they arrived on the day *the vet. gave up the possibility of a cure.*

We disregarded the box of M. & B.s and promptly fasted the calf, following word for word your instructions for this disease, with water and honey and seaweed powder and garlic tablets. The noise the calf made during the fasting period was rather a trial as we seemed to be guilty of starving the poor thing to death. But on the contrary. It gained strength and the discharge ceased, and the swelling at the navel also disappeared. We gradually introduced a normal ration of milk again, and the calf became well and strong again and is now just over 12 months old, and out on some hill land about 800 feet above sea-level and is very fit.

Later we cured a cow of slow fever, after orthodox treatment by the vet. had failed, and we did not hesitate to write for the necessary herbs, and again carefully followed your book as to treatment, and afterwards turned her out to grass. We have since parted with this cow but not through slow fever, but an injury to a teat causing trouble and making my wife extra work milking her by hand whilst I was in hospital.

Since the first cure of the calf we have used less provender than we used to and have found no cases of mastitis from which we always had some trouble.

Mr. C. A. M. West, Ardleigh Park Farm and Gardens, Colchester, Essex:

We bought a darned good near-pedigree Jersey in calf and she threw the calf on time without any trouble. This cow was intended for a house cow. We hope slowly to establish a Jersey herd. I kept the calf on its dam for eight days and it was right as rain. Then I put it on three pail feeds a day. I know that there is no substitute for a nurse cow but fixed as we are we just couldn't accommodate one at the moment. Otherwise, the calf was well cared for. I am pushed with work and had to cut out the midday feed after about ten days, giving about 9 1b. of milk in two feeds. After another few days the calf suddenly refused its evening feed and was very dopey with two degrees of temperature. I had to call an orthodox vet. He advised and gave M. & B. powder. I didn't like this but what could I do? I was worried about continuing to give milk, even watered milk as per the vet.'s instructions, as watered milk I have found often intensifies the binding. The M. & B. did, of course, reduce the temperature and the vet. advised three doses per diem until the bowels moved. I took the case in my own hands and in all the calf only got two doses of M. & B. I then fed it on mild barley water and gave it mild herbal laxatives and got the bowels going again, and for a few days it was almost normal. The vet. came again and advised a milk diet. I put the little beast back on watered milk and it developed serious staggers, throwing back its head and collapsing, then becoming quite normal. I had been looking out for the staggers, knowing the effect of an inflamed stomach on the brain. The vet. gave a sedative which decreased the intensity of the staggers but nothing was done to try to get the calf well. The form of staggers changed after two days and the calf couldn't use the front legs properly and went into 'reverse', exhibiting a spastic type of derangement. After that I had enough of vets. and called up you. The honey and water helped at once, probably easing the stomach, and I got the slippery elm and the calf seemed to turn the corner, the slippery elm obviously having a very soothing effect on the stomach. Then came your valuable herbs. There was an immediate effect for the better after the first dose of garlic, and the nervine eased the spasms of the front legs but the temperature was obviously sub-normal, after all the mucking about. I have continued using the garlic and rhubarb tablets, the latter every three days, just to keep the bowels moving. I have now reached the stage when I am finished off with slippery elm and going back again to three small feeds per day of milk, and the calf is well.

USERS OF MY VETERINARY METHODS

Mr. T. T. Stamm, Little Boarzell, Hurst Green, Sussex:

May I introduce myself by saying that I am a surgeon and a farmer. . . . I want to thank you for a good turn you have done me! One of my best cows failed repeatedly to hold to service. The Wellcome Research laboratories had her at their establishment for many weeks with no effect. After being dry for a year we tried your method of treatment. On the second service afterwards she held and is now safely in calf—so very many thanks!

Extract from letter from Mr. T. G. Richards, Quoit Gate, Brad-worthy, Holsworthy, Devon:

. . . In a large milking herd, such as the Ayrshire herd I managed in Gloucester, unless very close attention is paid to regular inspection of the cows, illnesses get out of hand before being discovered and then need more rigorous treatment. But by following your treatment with fasting and garlic by eighteen months after taking over I think I can honestly claim that mastitis had become a rarity, and provided it was treated along natural lines as soon as it appeared any slight loss of milk as a result of a fast was generally offset by the obvious improvement in the animal's condition and quite often subsequently increased milk output. If after the four days' fast there appeared to be no improvement, a warm water enema using garlic was given daily, and on the few occasions such drastic treatment was necessary it always did the trick. Garlic is given twice daily.

I find a twenty-four-hour fast with only water has a wonderful effect upon the animal. It also has a marvellous effect on an animal that is ailing or is disinterested in its food, and with garlic it is usually enough to cure an early attack of mastitis.

In a large commercial herd the value of such simple and effective treatment is great if one considers the fact that there are no vet.'s fees and no serums injected, and the subsequent increased good health of the animal.

I had one case which was first treated along orthodox lines without success. She was the highest yielder in the herd with a lactation of 16,311 lb. in 322 days, and tore one of her teats on barbed wire. It was sewn up—thirteen stitches—and she continued to milk well. She finished the lactation in which the accident occurred with 14,066 lb. at 3.66 percent in 304 days. She calved her sixth calf and gave 5,803 lb. in 123 days. Mastitis developed very suddenly—too suddenly for my liking and a conference was held as to whether my methods or the vet.'s should be used. As the whole herd was to be sold in about six weeks it was decided that the vet. should treat her. Penicillin was injected—but it made no difference to the quarter—it remained looking and feeling like a football and emitting a most noxious smell. The vet. washed his hands of her and the quarter was written off as useless.

I took her into a loose-box and then started treatment along natural lines but with the dice already heavily loaded against me. All food was stopped immediately, she was dosed with molasses and garlic and given cold water treatment on the affected quarter. Every three hours the quarter was stripped out and massaged for about ten minutes. For two weeks she was without any solid food and the above treatment carried out (or so I thought). As a result of the sale there was an end-of-the-term feeling about the farm and my treatment was not always faithfully and regularly carried out, but the swelling had almost completely disappeared by the day of the sale. There was, however, still a continuous suppuration of a pretty foul-smelling liquid.

She was sold for £10 and heading for the knacker's yard when I bought her for £25. Just prior to calving at the end of February 1951, and just after calving, she had two very slight attacks of mastitis and was subjected to two three-day fasts on garlic. As a result of this natural treatment she has now been able in her last lactation with me to produce never less than 5 gallons a day in forty weeks *on grass alone.*

STANLEY J. WILLIAMS, Glan-y-Mor Farms, Bow Street, Cardiganshire :

We have had many complete cures of mastitis, some of the worst type, and only three failures which were to be expected. Two of these were because it started before the animal calved and it had become too far gone by the time we spotted it. All four quarters were affected and the hardness, etc., was taken to be bagging up to calve. The third case was summer mastitis which was allowed to get too big a hold, and in fact the animal itself nearly died. We called in our veterinary surgeon to give us a picture of her clinical condition and his report was that he held little hope of the animal being alive by morning. We saved the animal at the expense of one quarter. We have been free now of the virulent mastitis for two years. We find now that the cows only have an occasional very mild attack (like a minor cold in a human) that one day's treatment puts right.

We have had marked success with the treatment of sterility, though I will confess that unless the animal is very valuable I find it less trouble and as economical to sell an animal, that is difficult to get in calf, as a barren. At the moment, of course, they sell as well empty as in calf. The method here is essentially the same as your treatment. Complete starvation for seven days but water given on the third day. In addition the anal and vaginal passages were syringed out twice a day with luke-warm water only. We find that by the second and third day of fasting the faeces evacuated tends to become very hard and the warm water syringing is extended. The animal's fast is broken very gradually on the eighth day with nothing but green food. No concentrates are given and no attempt should be made to fatten up the animal. One of our animals so treated calved last November, and will easily and with no forcing complete 1,000 gallons this lactation.

Another disease which causes us more loss of milk than any is foul foot or 'gibby'. This, like the other diseases, is elimination of waste matter and possibly it occurs in the hoof due to the excessive wetness in winter. The first symptoms are lameness, and inflammation of the hoof and ankle, which finally bursts in between the claws or at the top of the hoof. We have tried many different treatments, but all require three or four days and though no doubt the cow would benefit greatly from a twenty-four or forty-eight-hour fast we don't find it essential. The easiest method is hosing the foot with cold water four times a day, i.e. when the animal comes into the shed in the morning, and then after milking, then in the afternoon before milking and after milking before turning out. We have tried hot bran poultices, hot Kaolin, plain hot water. But all these are far more laborious and no whit more effective than ordinary cold water from a hose pipe.

The numerous cuts, abrasions and gashes caused by horning, all these are cured with us by turning on the cold water hose. When we first started our old cowman was a scoffer. Now he always goes for it on all occasions and he points to the hose-pipe and says: 'Best vet.—that!'

Mr. Mark Fitzroy, Lower Oak Farm, Okehampton, Devon:

You will be glad to hear that the cow we fasted and treated according to your advice has calved down all right with no sign of mastitis in the milk.

Mr. Russell Bailey, Croft House, Chapelthorpe, Nr. Wakefield:

I am glad to be able to tell you that we have been exceedingly free from mastitis, and have had no case of sterility. I certainly attribute that to the way in which the animals have been fed and treated.

About three months ago, we did have one bad case of mastitis which was not noticed until it had become acute, because it happened during our very difficult harvest when the milking was not as closely supervised as usual. However, immediately my son discovered the position, we followed out the instructions contained in your booklet to the letter.

Later—Mr. Bailey wrote:

I have completely cured the Ayrshire cow of mastitis by following the instructions in your books. I am an engineer and not a farmer, but I fasted her for four days and even bought a syringe and gave her enemas, and of course garlic. My old farm man was certain I should kill the cow. Now he thinks I am a magician!

R. V. Ling, Oak Farm, Danehill, Sussex:

I am grateful to you for advice on the treatment of scour in calves.

A two-week-old Jersey calf born on the farm developed white scour, apparently infected by a calf which had just been bought and was scouring. A patent remedy and a vet.'s prescription were tried in turn but after about ten days there was no improvement and the trouble had affected two more calves in spite of isolation. No alteration in feeding had been made as all calves were suckling naturally.

I then had your advice and the following day kept the Jersey calf entirely off food for twenty-four hours; the second day she was given three feeds of not more than five minutes each and by the end of that day evacuation was completely normal. The other three calves were given the same treatment and cured; there was no recurrence.

Some months ago I lost a good Jersey calf through white scour and previous experience had left me very dissatisfied with orthodox treatment. Apart from scientific justification there is the same sense of rightness about your method as there is about organic methods of maintaining soil fertility; and both cases pass the crucial test—they work.

USERS OF MY VETERINARY METHODS

Mr. L. C. Abrahams, Woodlands Farm, Headley, Nr. Newbury:

You may remember that I phoned you about ten days before Xmas to ask you about your treatment of Johne's disease outlined in *Fertility Farming.* In this case the vet. advised slaughter.

The animal affected was a home-bred Guernsey heifer of about eighteen months, and this was the second case on the farm, the other being in an old Jersey, occurring in January 1950 after I had her about six months.

I carried out your course of treatment, and told my vet. I was doing so; he was professionally dismayed but in order, as he said, 'to encourage such an experiment', he offered to have the dung samples tested and cultures prepared from them free of charge.

I am glad to be able to tell you that he rang me this morning to say that the report had just come in saying that they could find *no* trace of the disease.

Needless to say, to us, seeing this animal from day to day and noting her very obvious improvement once she came on to food again this was not unexpected. She looks twice the animal she did.

Please accept my thanks for your help, both verbal and written. If you are ever in these parts and care to call we should be very glad to see you.

Yours gratefully …

Mr. A. E. K. Cull, Llwyndu Court, Abergavenny, Monmouthshire.

I feel I must write and tell you about 'Rose.' You will remember that she was an old cow about 12 or 13 years old, and that we had for a year or so continuously failed to get her in calf. A leading veterinary consultant and sterility specialist recommended having her put down.

Mr. Bennett then asked you to come and see her and you told us about your treatment. We carried this out twice and about a month ago she had a bull calf. She seems to be doing well now.

I thought I must write and give you our most grateful thanks.

Appendix 2

THE WHY AND HOW OF THE BREEDS

Though Shorthorns were my first love, Jerseys were my ultimate choice, and the breed which I know really well. Though, as a student of cattle breeding, I am a keen observer of the performances of all breeds, I cannot claim impartiality in advising on the choice of breed. So I have asked eight well-known breeders to write about their breeds from their first-hand experience. I have added information on the breed points supplied by the breed societies. Much of this section has already appeared in *The Farmer,* the organic farming quarterly.

JERSEYS

When I decided that pedigree cattle were as cheap to keep as mongrels, and what is far more important, a good deal dearer to sell, the problem of choosing a breed was not easy. I had been reared on heavy breeds and so I started with a strong prejudice against the Jersey. It was the purchase of two cheap first-calf heifers for the house which demonstrated to me the amazing ability of these little animals to convert food into milk at a remarkably low cost.

I bought a few more and proceeded to keep careful records of food consumption in relation to milk production of the three breeds which I then had, Shorthorn, Friesian, and the crosses of these two, compared with the Jersey.

The following figures which give the only true test of a cow, that is cost per gallon, in relation to body weight, indicated more clearly to me than any examination with the eye or prejudice of the mind, that if milk production was to be my business then the Jersey must be my breed.

Approximate Body Weight	Name of Cow	Breed	Yield	Cost per gallon	
lb.			lb.	s.	d.
1,250	Annabelle	Shorthorn	$9,819\frac{1}{2}$	1	3
1,200	Prosperous 2nd	Shorthorn × Friesian	$8,368\frac{3}{4}$	1	6
1,400	Beauty	Shorthorn × Friesian	17,256	1	0
1,300	Prosperous	Friesian	13,808	1	4
850	Fair Aldan	Jersey	$11,721\frac{3}{4}$		7
700	June Rose	Jersey	$8,002\frac{3}{4}$		$8\frac{1}{2}$
750	Poppy	Jersey	8,733		$7\frac{1}{2}$
700	Yetanother	Jersey	8,890		8

2006 Currency*

Approximate Body Weight	Name of Cow	Breed	Yield	Cost per gallon	
lb.			lb.	£	1.85
1,250	Annabelle	Shorthorn	$9,819\frac{1}{2}$	$	3.40
1,200	Prosperous 2nd	Shorthorn × Friesian	$8,368\frac{3}{4}$	£	2.22
				$	4.08
1,400	Beauty	Shorthorn × Friesian	17,256	£	1.48
				$	2.67
1,300	Prosperous	Friesian	13,808	£	1.98
				$	3.64
850	Fair Aldan	Jersey	$11,721\frac{3}{4}$	£	0.87
				$	1.93
700	June Rose	Jersey	$8,002\frac{3}{4}$	£	1.05
				$	1.93
750	Poppy	Jersey	8,733	£	0.93
				$	1.71
700	Yetanother	Jersey	8,890	£	0.99
				$	1.82

*Editor's note: The author's historic financial data was converted to modern currencies and approximately adjusted for inflation, using the consumer price index. This most certainly will not correlate to modern costs and prices, but should be utilized for general directional trends only.

It should be noted that these costs were calculated in 1945 when prices were considerably lower than they are today. They were arrived at by a daily recording of milk yielded and total food fed. The cost of food fed to each cow was added to an averaged labour cost per cow and this figure was divided by the gallonage of milk given in the lactation. It should not be forgotten that the cost of labour for the cows needing more food would undoubtedly be higher, but as I could evolve no way of apportioning so exactly the labour, an average labour cost had to be used. I could, of course, have apportioned labour costs according to the amount of food fed but at the time I felt this too involved. Additionally it should be borne in mind that the price realizable for Jersey milk is at least 4d. a gallon more than most other breeds because of the quality (i.e. butterfat) premium.

What are the reasons for the remarkable efficiency of the Jersey? Well, there are many.

Health

The Jersey, unlike almost any other breed of dairy cow, except perhaps the Guernsey and the Kerry, has not suffered from exploitive methods of management. Until recently, that is almost right up to the war, the Jersey farmer has practised a balanced system of farming and has fed his cows naturally with no attempt to extract excessive yields of milk. Only one or two of the larger herds concentrated on milk yield, and even then not at the expense of butterfat and type. Similarly in this country the Jersey was in the hands of breeders who considered high milk yields unimportant, for in view of the Jersey's inability to convert food to body fat, she was always in any case an economical and efficient producer. Consequently the majority of Jerseys have an inheritance of health and sound constitution.

The old fallacy that Jerseys are delicate has been long disproved. It probably arose in the first place because wealthy people who kept a few cows for the house treated them as pets and the onlooker assumed that such treatment was essential. The fact that the Jersey more than any other breed shows remarkable sleekness of coat after being rugged has also encouraged breeders to make too much use of the rug at shows, and this of course has fostered the belief that the Jersey is delicate. Commercial farmers have, however, now discovered the remarkable hardiness and adaptability of the Jersey.

My animals live almost entirely out of doors, and under such conditions they grow thick shaggy protective coats which retain body heat in winter so effectively that in extremely frosty weather they often come in to milking with white hoar frost and icicles on their hair.

Long Productive Life

The Jersey is early maturing and will produce a calf and 700 or so gallons of milk before most other breeds calve down. But I don't stick too strictly to a rigid bulling age. Though fifteen months (to calve the first calf at two years old) is no doubt the ideal for a well-grown heifer, I have them bulled at from fifteen to twenty months old according to growth and general condition.

Longevity is a valuable characteristic of the Jersey, and this again is due to the freedom from exploitation and artificial feeding almost right up to 1940, in the Jersey breed. Given a reasonably natural existence, especially with regard to rearing and feeding, the Jersey will produce economically and breed consistently up to the age of fourteen to twenty. I have a number of cattle between those ages, and one now twenty-two years old, and I expect all my home-bred cattle to serve me efficiently up to the age of twenty.

Butterfat Demand

The Jersey is supreme as a producer of butterfat, a fact which I believe is in some way related to the extensive use of seaweed in manuring the soil of Jersey. The factor in food which goes to the making of fat in the case of the Jersey appears to convert all food to butterfat rather than body fat, at any rate during lactation. No one has yet explained the relationship of food to milk fat and body fat but there is no question about the difficulty of fattening a Jersey compared with every other breed, or the supremacy of the Jersey as a converter of foodstuffs to butterfat. It just happens that with the Jersey there is some unknown factor which transfers the food the cow consumes via the udder to the bucket, instead of on to the ribs. And while there is a choice of breed it doesn't matter if we cannot discover this secret.

In open competition with other breeds, particularly in production tests, the Jersey has also demonstrated its supremacy.

The two most important competitions in the dairy farming world are the Harold Jackson Trophy and the National Milk Cup. Each has in the last fifteen years gone more often to the Jersey than to any other breed. The Jersey is the only breed to have won the Harold Jackson Trophy as many as five years in succession. The Harold Jackson Trophy is awarded to the cow of any breed gaining most points for milk and butterfat over a period of three years. The National Milk Cup is awarded to the cow of any breed yielding the most milk and butterfat in relation to bodyweight. It is the only National Trophy which gives a true test of efficient production, though I understand there is an International Trophy shortly to be presented by the well-known cattle judge, R. W. (Bob) Carson, for annual competition which will take account of all relevant factors. All other trophies are awarded for yield regardless of body weight, which, where cost of production is to be considered, means nothing. The real test of the breeds is the efficiency of the cow as a converter of food into milk and butterfat and in this respect, both in any costings that have been carried out, and in open competition where the ratio of body weight is taken into account, the Jersey has so far proved supreme.

How

My own methods of animal husbandry are simple, and they are elaborated in other parts of this book. They are based on an attempt to breed, rear and generally keep the cow under conditions as near to natural as possible. This is the only way to breed the solid structure of health which is essential to efficient production. With each generation I can be more certain of an inheritance of health without which it is useless to select and breed for profitable milk production. By these methods I have eliminated the greatest drains on the income of the dairy farm which are losses from disease and the vet.'s bill (except for tests which are necessitated by official schemes and sales).

Except in emergency the animals are fed on home-grown food, the basis of which in the summer is the herbal ley containing as wide a variety of herbs as it is possible to obtain. Each year I seek sources of herbs hitherto unused in the ley to incorporate in the mixture. I believe that garlic taken in small quantities, in conjunction with other herbs, will prove immensely beneficial to the cow, without tainting the milk. It is when it is taken in large quantities alone, on occasion when the cow finds this valuable herb in a formerly undiscovered corner, that she gorges herself with relish and in consequence taints her milk.

Seaweeds of various kinds form the best mineral supplement, used as a manure on the land, or in dry powdered form in the meal ration, being organic and quite harmless.

In the winter the basis of the maintenance ration is silage, which is fed in quantities up to 60 1b. each daily according to availability and requirements. Oat straw forms the dry bulky food necessary to assist cudding,

173

and this is cut on the green side and tripodded, so that in feeding value it is equal to much of the hay at present made in this country. Having assured the ample bulky food which is natural and essential to the health of the cow, production ration made up of three lbs. of ground oats, and one lb. of linseed is the normal allowance per gallon of milk after the second gallon.

No animal is fed to yield more than her inherent capacity, that is, what she will give on entirely home-grown food of low protein ratio. Excessive protein feeding, in concentrated form, over-stimulates the cow, and results in the digestive troubles such as acetonaemia. Yet my herd average had reached 813 gallons last year (excluding two animals which were in the herd for treatment).

All calves are reared on cows, a system which I consider imperative to the future health of my herd. The foundation of vigorous life is laid by nature via the dam in the first weeks and months of life, and to deprive any living thing of its natural food, containing essential elements and vital forces which are incapable of human measurement or substitution, is to guarantee disease and infertility in future life.

The leys which are the basis of all our feeding are planned primarily for grazing, and hay or silage are taken when, as invariably happens each summer, one of the paddocks grows ahead of the herd. Other crops are grown for silage, mainly oats and vetches, and a few acres of lucerne are kept for green feeding, silage or tripodded hay.

The leys are divided into paddocks of 3 to 4 acres each with an electric fence, and grazing is continuous at the rate of about ten cows to the acre. A field is kept from mid-August until November and then strip grazed through November, December, January and February, allowing a few yards, across the full width of the field, each day. Grazing in this way, and with the ample herbs in the mixture, there is no risk of blowing, a trouble which is common with leys of simple seeds mixtures without the herbs. More detailed feeding calculations are given in the chapter, 'Feeding the Dairy Herd'.

Given this basis of natural diet, it is rarely we find any veterinary treatment is needed. Should there be any minor illness, resulting from carelessness, temptation to overfeed, inherited predisposition to certain complaints like mastitis and sterility, we are not troubled for more than a matter of hours. Immediate fasting combined with the herbal treatment set out in the latter part of this book, will effect quick and complete cure. These pages describe the simple natural treatment of most cattle diseases, authenticated by the experience of many other successful users of my methods.

On a basis of sound health and constitution we rely on selection and breeding for raising our herd average, rather than upon the feeding of high

35. The Guernsey bull.

36. The Guernsey cow.

37. The Dairy Shorthorn bull.

38. The Dairy Shorthorn cow.

protein concentrates, or limitation of bulk in the ration. A high herd average which is built on artificial methods such as overfeeding with stimulating foods, encouraging the animal by 'pre-milking' to give milk before she gives a calf, and other artificial perversions of nature, can in the long run achieve nothing but the unbalancing of the reproductive system, a condition which is already evident in the widespread breeding troubles among dairy cattle. My methods improve yields by selection for health, constitution, butter-fat, and type, as well as mere milk.

WHAT TO LOOK FOR IN A JERSEY

Points of the Bull

	points
Head—Broad, fine; horns small and incurving; eye full and lively	5
Muzzle—Broad, encircled by a light colour, nostrils high and open; cheek, small	5
Neck—Arched, powerful and clean at the throat	7
Withers—Fine; shoulders flat and sloping	5
Lung—Capacity as indicated by depth and breadth immediately behind the shoulders	8
Barrel—Deep, broad and long, denoting large capacity; ribs rounding in shape	12
Back—Straight from withers to setting of tail; croup and setting on not coarse	10
Hips—Wide apart, rather prominent and fine in the bone	5
Loins—Broad and strong	5
Legs—Rather short, fine in the bone, squarely placed and not to cross or sweep in walking	5
Teats—Rudimentary, squarely placed and wide apart	5
Tail—Thin, reaching the hocks with good switch;	2
Well grown according to age	3
Hide—Thin, loose and mellow;	5
Showing a yellow colour on skin and horns	3
General appearance—Denoting a high class male animal, typical, and of a class suitable for reproduction	15
Total	100

Points of the Cow

	points
Head—Fine; face dished; cheek fine; throat clean	4
Nostrils—High and open; muzzle encircled by a light colour	2
Horns—small and incurving; eye full and placid	2

177

Neck—Straight, thin and long, and lightly placed on shoulders	5
Lung—Capacity as indicated by width and depth through body immediately behind the shoulders	3
Barrel—Deep, broad and long, denoting large capacity; ribs rounding in shape	10
Back—Straight from withers to setting of tail, croup and setting on not coarse	6
Withers—Fine and not coarse at point of shoulders	4
Hips—Wide apart, rather prominent and fine in the bone	2
Hind Legs—Squarely placed when viewed from behind and not to cross or sweep in walking	2
Tail—Thin, reaching the hocks, good switch	2
Udder—Large, not fleshy, and well balanced	10
Fore-udder—Full and running well forward	10
Rear-udder—Well up, protruding behind and not rounding abruptly at the top	8
Teats—Of good uniform length and size, wide apart and squarely placed	7
Milk Veins—Large and prominent	3
Richness—As indicated by yellow colour on horns, escutcheons and inside of ears	3
Skin—Thin, loose and mellow	4
Growth	3
General Appearance—Denoting a high class and economical dairy cow	10

Total   100

GUERNSEYS

by G. F. DEE SHAPLAND

It is indeed difficult to answer in a few words why I keep Guernseys, but I think the best way is to give the various points, and then to elaborate upon each.

1. The Guernsey is hardy.
2. Guernseys thrive well on poor land.
3. They produce large quantities of rich golden milk which receives a bonus of 4d. or more per gallon.
4. Early maturity and docility are common to the breed.
5. Guernseys have long life and freedom from disease.
6. They are easy milkers, with udders that collapse well after milking.

That the Guernsey is hardy cannot be denied as she is found all over this country from Cornwall to Scotland, in U.S.A., Canada, South Africa, Kenya, Australia, to mention just a few of the climates that suit her.

Many herds are maintained out of doors all the year round, indeed one on the Scottish border, over 600 feet up, averages 1,000 gallons a year under commercial conditions. With my own herd they come in at night when the pastures get too wet, not for the cow's sake, but because of the poaching that would otherwise occur.

Calf Rearing

Calves are all weaned at three days, and bucket-fed from the dam's milk, usually four pints per feed, twice daily. The heifer calf continues with this, and a little fine hay when old enough, for two months, when a milk substitute is added pint for pint of the milk, with a little cake and meal, until the calf is entirely on milk substitute. At five months they are weaned entirely from the bucket and then get a mixture of dredge corn (rolled) with a little linseed cake, calf cake, bran, flake maize, etc., as available, to which is added Cod Liver Oil, and 1 percent of minerals. Mineral salt licks are always available. The calves have a 'good do' until twelve months old, when they are turned out, and do not come home again until four weeks from calving. Our heifers get no other food from twelve months old, but hay and grass, and we find they have done equally as well as their predecessors before the war, that had a cake ration.

It is not necessary to have a very rich farm for Guernseys, indeed some of the best results have come from herds maintained on poor farms. Very rich conditions are sometimes responsible for a fattening of the young stock and milking herd, and under these conditions much milk is often lost. The cows work better in a good hard condition.

Heifers calve in from two to three years, and are bred according to size more than age. I consider here that heifers should average at least three gallons per day, which at two years old (nine months to a year earlier than some breeds), and receiving 4d. per gallon over pool price, makes the breed a very commercial proposition. The breed is excellent when subjected to the Tuberculin Test, and most Guernsey herds are attested.

Cream Line

T.T. Guernsey milk is a good seller, and it is true to say that once a housewife has had a good supply she will not readily have any other. She looks for the golden cream line on the bottle. Many herds of Guernseys have been started by the retailer asking the farmer to improve his quality and colour; a few Guernseys are mixed with the herd, and usually do so well that a complete herd is formed. Travelling around the country, one sees a large number of herds that contain one or two Guernseys, which signifies that not only does the churn benefit, but the farmer's wife enjoys some 'golden butter'.

Docility

Guernsey cattle are very docile and are equally happy tethered or running loose. This tethering, so useful on grass verges, poultry pens, etc., encourages the extreme docility, or rather friendliness of the animals. Heifers coming home for the first time are soon led by a halter, and tied up without any trouble. Bulls should always be tethered. Never run them loose, as this encourages the natural protective spirit, and often makes handling difficult later on.

The cows are easy milkers with an udder that collapses well after milking, and the breed appears to take well to either hand or machine.

A commercial herd should have no trouble in maintaining an 800 gallon average, and a calf a year. My average here for 1949 is 970 gallons in 305 days, average butterfat 4.69. Five heifers averaged 898 gallons, calving index, 378 days. The herd average includes two old cows, twelve and thirteen years, from which we tried to breed just one more calf, these old ones always reduce our average, which has been over 900 gallons for the past sixteen years.

Our herd was exhibited before the war with great success, many championships being won, but perhaps the best performances were the winning of the Harold Jackson trophy in 1936 with a home-bred cow, and winning with 'Cis of North Valley' the supreme production championship at the Bath and West Show at Bridgwater in 1939. Cis gave over 75 lb. of milk, and churned over 4 lb. of butter in twenty-four hours.

The herd is closely bred, a number of cows, daughters of the famous 'Camilla's Majestic III of Maple Lodge', were bred to a half-brother with success, and now to a grandson 'Zenita's Dairyman of the Fontaines'.

The herd is maintained at about 56 head on 90 acres.

The Cow I Want

Big cows with fine bone, with great capacity are favoured, and are maintained in a lean condition.

Cows that put flesh on their backs are not favoured, as I consider that this animal cannot look after her back and put fat into the udder.

The Guernsey breed has gained many new members during the past few years, and membership of the E.G.C.S. is about 3,000. The terrific demand for "Golden Milk," rich milk with a delightful flavour all its own, ensures that the breed will continue to attract commercial farmers in ever increasing numbers. If a surplus of milk should ever come back to this country, it is true to say that Guernsey milk will always sell as a liquid, but if your farm is off the map and delivery is difficult you can always fall back on the manufacture of cream which has always had a ready sale, and of course leaves the skim milk for pig feeding, and the return of manure to the farm, which is good farming, much in need at the moment.

To sum up, the Guernsey is a beautiful clean-looking and docile cow that thrives well under most conditions, and it is only necessary to buy one to become an enthusiast and form a herd.

WHAT TO LOOK FOR IN A GUERNSEY

The Points of a Cow

	points
Size—Cows, four years old or over, about 1,000 lb. weight	3
General Appearance—(or type)—Fine throughout, lean fleshed and not fat, of hardy and symmetrical appearance, frame smoothly covered with muscle, body deep, wide through hindquarters, wedge-shaped whether viewed from in front, the side, or behind	6
Quality—(general)—Good carriage, fine clean bone	3
Legs—Fine, well apart, medium length, wide curve from flank to hock joint, hocks parallel and wide apart; legs free in motion with no tendency to sweep or turn	2
Quality—(touch)—Skin thin, mellow and loose to the touch, well and closely covered with fine hair	3
Colour—A shade of fawn with or without white markings	2
Head—Head fine and long; lean face, broad between the eyes; eyes large with quiet gentle expression; muzzle broad, flesh coloured nose; horns fine and curved	5
Neck—Long and thin, clean throat	3

Shoulders—Shoulders fine, backbone rising well between
    shoulder-blades; chine fine   3
Chest—Deep and wide between and behind forelegs, girth full.
    Ribs long, deep and wide apart   7
Back—Level to tail-head; broad and level across loins and hips   3
Hindquarters—Rump long, wide and level; hook bones wide apart.
    Thighs long and flat; tail fine, reaching to hocks, good switch   10
Udder—(a) udder level and full in front (8); (b) udder full
    and well up behind (8); (c) udder of large size and capacity, elastic, silky
    and not fleshy (8); (d) teats well apart, squarely placed, and of good and
    even size (7)   31
Veins and Wells—Milk veins prominent, long tortuous, with large and deep
    wells; escutcheon wide, with thigh ovals, and wide on thighs   9
Skin—Yellow in ear, at base of horns, on end of tail, on udder, teats
    and body generally, hoofs amber coloured   10

Total   100

For inspection a jet-black nose is disqualification. Judges will have power to penalize an animal showing an excessive amount of flesh, and in particular, heifers which have had a calf whose appearance suggests that they have been fed more highly than their age warrants in consideration of their future life as milking animals.

Dehorned animals will not be penalized.

The Points of a Bull

points

Size—Bulls, four years or over, about 1,500 lb. weight   6
General Appearance—(or type)—Masculine throughout, frame well
    furnished with muscle characteristic of a male animal but not beefy; body
    deep, of good length, wide through hindquarters; vigorous and alert and
    symmetrical in appearance   10
Quality—(general)—Good carriage; fine clean bone   5
Legs—Fine, well apart, medium length, wide curve from flank to hock joints,
    hocks parallel and wide apart; legs free in motion with no tendency to
    sweep or turn   5
Quality—(touch)—Skin thin, mellow and loose to the touch, well and closely
    covered with fine hair   5

Colour—A shade of fawn with or without white markings 5
Head—Masculine, but not coarse, clean-cut, lean face, broad between the eyes;
    bright eyes, quiet gentle expression and strong sinewy jaw; muzzle broad,
    flesh coloured nose; horns medium 8
Neck—Long, with well-developed crest, clean throat 5
Shoulders—Powerful, clean, fine at top, backbone rising well between
    shoulder-blades; chine fine 5
Chest—Deep and wide between and behind forelegs, girth full.
    Ribs long, deep and wide apart 10
Back—Level to tail-head, broad and level across loins;
    broad between the hips 8
Hindquarters—Rump long, wide and level; hook-bones wide apart;
    thighs long and fiat, muscular but not beefy; tail fine, reaching
    to hocks, good switch 10
Teats—Of fair size, wide apart and squarely placed; Escutcheon:
    well developed 8
Skin—Yellow in ear, at base of horns, on end of tail, and body generally;
    hoofs amber coloured 10

Total   100

For inspection purposes a jet-black nose is a disqualification. Judges will have power to penalize any animal showing an excessive amount of flesh.

Dehorned animals will not be penalized.

DAIRY SHORTHORNS

by ROBERT HOBBS

Why do I keep Dairy Shorthorns? Is it because my father and grand-father kept them before me? Or from the fact that the Shorthorn is the breed of this country for which England has been famed for 150 years? They have held sway at my farm for over seventy years; but I ould hardly feel justified in continuing to breed Shorthorns were I not fully convinced that they are the soundest cattle proposition for the future with farmers in this country. Dual-purpose cattle we must have if we are to get the fullest amount of beef and milk which we are capable of producing. Our future beef stores must come largely from our dairy herds, and no breed is more fitted to produce the quality of milk most suited for home consumption, and, at the same time give us suitable grazing stores.

183

Milk Surplus Coming

With modern knowledge of expert ley farming the grazing capacity of our land could be more than doubled. No country has the soil and climatic conditions more suitable for a vast production of beef and mutton throughout the summer were the stock forthcoming, and the storage for the meat available at the close of the grazing season. The Government demand for milk and more milk throughout the war years together with the abnormally high prices for milk and cereals have unbalanced our farming; and many farmers are relying too much for a living on their milk cheque, and on low-yielding cereal crops.

A surplus of milk for home consumption is already becoming evident, and the country cannot face the loss of manufacturing milk into cheese or milk powder at current prices.

Still the Best Dual-Purpose Cow

Docile and easily managed, no breed fits better into the general farm routine, or converts the home-grown food more economically into milk and beef than the Dairy Shorthorn.

When milk prices fall the man with the sound dual-purpose cow will best hold his own; and for this reason the milking Shorthorn should always predominate amongst the general run of British farmers. For, apart from her milk, she will feed readily into an evenly fleshed beef carcass. Her good natural coat enables her to winter out day and night on light soils, as will also her offspring if required.

Steers from Dairy Shorthorns are now seen in many Shorthorn herds, and they clearly demonstrate the good fleshing qualities of their dams.

How They Are Managed

Our herd at Kelmscott numbers 240 head, of which about 70 cows are in milk. They are run like an ordinary well-managed commercial herd, sharing the grazing and home-grown food with the other livestock on the 800 acre farm. Apart from the Shorthorns there is a flock of 200 half-bred ewes with their 380 odd lambs, 20 pedigree Wessex-Saddleback breeding sows with a large stock of breeding gilts and baconers, whilst 1,000 hens in folding units are continually on the grass leys.

The milking herd graze the three- to four-year leys, moving back to an old pasture after one or two hours on the ley, after milking morning and evening. Autumn sown winter oats or wheat often give three or four weeks' feed to the cows in early spring previous to going on to the grass leys.

An old pasture is available for occupation day and night throughout the winter. Maintenance food in the shape of silage, hay, oat straw, kale or mangold is fed in the fields after milking.

The young stock are wintered in covered yards, getting little beyond hay, straw, silage and mangolds. Dry, in-calf cows winter in the fields, as do the spring-calving heifers. Calves are taken off their dams at the fourth day, and are reared on the pail; but there are usually ten or twelve calves getting their milk twice daily from five or six off-going cows. Bull calves get a strictly limited milk ration, except possibly two or three individuals selected for the summer shows.

Reared in this manner, the young bulls are not forced for sale by auction, but are sold privately at home in good ordinary breeding condition. The large milking herd of 70 cows is in one unit, and is machine milked twice daily. Under such conditions good but not abnormal yields are expected. The last year's average yield as given by National Milk Record shows 55 cows to average 8,730 lb., 21 heifers average 7,527 lb. Kelmscott-Meoly 107th heads the County Shorthorn tests with a yield of 20,432 lb. in 305 days with 701 lb. of butter. This cow, although running with the main herd, was milked three times daily. No herd can boast of a longer or more successful showyard career. The first Royal Show Championship was won forty years ago in 1909. At the Royal in 1949 all three of the Group Challenge Cups were won by home-bred cattle from the Kelmscott herd. Careful line breeding permits the use of home-bred sires to a large extent. Of the eight sires now in service, five of them are home-bred.

The leading sire today is the twelve-year-old white Kelmscott Gay Baron 24th, an I.R.M. bull. At ten years old he was Champion at the Oxfordshire show. He is out of the Royal Champion cow Kelmscott Marjory 47. He was sired by Histon Gay Barrington whose dam Elkston Barrington Duchess was first at the Royal in 1936, being placed Reserve to Kelmscott Marjory 47 for the Female Championship.

Amongst Kelmscott Gay Baron 24th's most noted progeny are Kelmscott Pink 22nd, winner of first prize at the Royal and Supreme Champion at the Three Counties Show in 1947; Kelmscott Betty 53rd, Champion Royal Counties Show, 1949; Kelmscott Solo 169th, First at Royal Show, 1949; and First and Reserve Champion Bath and West Show, 1950; Kelmscott Gay Lord 40th, Champion at the Suffolk Show, 1949; and Kelmscott Pink

158th, First and Female Champion Shropshire and West Midland Show; and Female and Supreme Champion at Bath and West Show, 1950.

WHAT TO LOOK FOR IN A DAIRY SHORTHORN

Points of the Bull

Head—Masculine in character (not too short); horns flat and well set on without coarseness at base, forehead broad, eyes large and bold, muzzle wide with nostrils large and expansive, nose flesh coloured and clear of black or blue markings, throat clearly defined.

Neck—Long, arched and muscular, but not heavy.

Withers—Strong but not too wide.

Shoulders—Neat and sloping.

Chest—Broad and deep, not running light at the girth.

Barrel—Deep with ribs well sprung.

Back—Broad, strong loins, the top line being straight from withers to tail.

Hips—Wide apart and free from coarseness.

Rump—Long, broad and level, with pin bones as wide as possible, tail neatly set in.

Hindquarters—When viewed from behind should be wide, hocks straight and without nearness when walking.

Rudimentary Teats—Well developed, set horizontally, wide apart, and away from the scrotum.

Skin—Flexible and of mellow touch, carrying a good coat of hair, patchy or faded colours being avoided.

Flesh—Level with an entire absence of unevenness or cushions.

Carriage and action in walking, gay and vigorous.

General appearance symmetrical combining size and scope.

Points of the Cow

Head—Feminine in character, horns fine, curved inward and small at base, forehead broad, eyes large and of gentle expression, muzzle wide with nostrils large and expansive, nose flesh coloured and clear of black or blue markings, throat clearly defined.

Neck—Lean but not weak with sufficient length for good head carriage.

Withers—Not too wide.

Shoulders—Neat and sloping.

Chest—Broad and deep, not running light at the girth.

Barrel—Deep with ribs well sprung.

Back—Broad, strong loin, the top line being straight from withers to tail.

Hips—Wide apart and free from coarseness.

Rump—Long, broad and level, with pin bones as wide as possible, tail fine and neatly set in.

Hindquarters—When viewed from behind should be wide, hocks straight without nearness when walking.

Udder—Well carried, thin skinned with pronounced milk veins, large in capacity (not fleshy or split up between the quarters), extending high up and back, hanging almost perpendicularly, and running well forward in a line with the belly, teats of good and even size, squarely placed and wide apart, milk veins highly developed and carried well forward, ending in large milk wells.

Skin—Flexible and of mellow touch and carrying a good coat of hair, patchy or faded colours being avoided.*

Flesh—Level, with entire absence of unevenness or cushions.

Carriage and action in walking, gay.

General appearance symmetrical, combining size and scope.

* *The recognised colour descriptions of Shorthorn cattle are as follows—red, red and white, red and little white, roan, dark roan, red roan, light roan or white.*

KERRYS

by Joan Cochrane

I was lucky to come in contact with Kerry cattle early in my farming days, or I might like so many other people have thought of them as a 'fancy' breed and not realized their great merit.

It is often pointed out that the Kerry is suitable for poor land where other cattle wouldn't thrive, and although this is true, and they will live and do well in poor, rough country, this doesn't mean that they won't do a lot better on good land. With proper feeding and management their yield compares very favourably with that of the other dairy breeds and yet the Kerry has a much smaller stomach capacity and needs far less bulk than the larger types and you can keep a greater head of stock on your acreage than any other breed except perhaps the Jersey and their fellow-country-man the Dexter. There has been a tendency to breed Kerries rather bigger in this country but I believe the economical size for a Kerry is no bigger than a Jersey, say about 750 lb. mature live weight. If we tried to force the Kerry I am sure she would give a staggering yield for her size, but there is no need for this; fed on one's own home-grown foods for every gallon over the first in winter and providing you have good grass in the summer, she will probably need no supplementary feeding to give a really good economic supply of excellent quality milk which, possessing a very small fat globule, is renowned for its digestibility.

Level Yielders

Maybe she will only give four to five gallons daily at the height of her lactation, although many give more, but she will keep this up right through, and when the time comes to dry her off, she will probably still be giving about two gallons a day, having already given a really good yield with very little extra feeding. It is not unusual for a Kerry to have given over 1,000 gallons in a lactation period of from anything between 305 to 365 days, without ever having exceeded four and a half gallons per day. There will be no need to sell off or kill off your cow after a few lactations; she will go on for many years calving regularly, and even improving in the quantity of milk as she gets older. One of my cows gave 1,000 gallons last year for the first time with her ninth calf. I feel there should be a place for the Kerry on the Exmoor hill farms and on much other marginal land; surely the type of country and climate is very similar to that of their native Co. Kerry? It may not be dairying country, but this hardy little cow is well able to stand up to the rigorous conditions and give a very useful supply of milk, or rear healthy calves.

My Methods

Though I agree that organic methods of management are the ideal from the point of view of the health of the animals, it is often difficult on the small farm to practise them always economically. Nevertheless I do try to rear my calves as naturally as possible, and whenever we have cows which we can spare as foster mothers we find this way better for the calf and more economical of labour.

$1\frac{1}{4}$ Acres per Head

You can imagine that on my 85 acres of land it is not possible to be self-supporting in feeding stuffs for 60 head of cattle. But rations do not enable us to overfeed on purchased cakes, with so many mouths to share them. So that the whole of the farm is devoted to growing food for the Kerries, and I am at the moment wondering whether I should cut down the milking herd and be self-sufficient in food, or maintain my present herd of stock and continue to buy some of it. Self-sufficiency is obviously the safe insurance and the best policy from a long term point of view. There is no doubt that by growing my own food entirely I shall be assuring the future health of my herd, but the demand for Kerries is so great that one is encouraged to rear as many cattle as possible to maturity and lay good health foundations by doing them well as calves.

Thirty acres of the farm are arable at the moment and the rest is permanent grass, some of it almost useless in its present condition. But when I can get this old grass broken and reseeded to good mixtures my supply of home-grown food should be nearly doubled. Nothing demonstrated the value of leys more than the drought of 1949. But it has also demonstrated how well these little Kerry cattle thrive on bare pastures. Although the pastures are old there is no rough herbage wasted. Traditionally they have been accustomed to rough coarse pastures with little growth to wrap their tongues around. These are the conditions of the native heath of the Kerry in Ireland.

Milkers and Prizewinners

But brought on to only moderate pastures and with the limited food of the rationing system, the Kerry will milk as well as most breeds, with less trouble and at far less cost per gallon of milk. Some of my own Kerries have demonstrated what can be done with this breed by careful selective breeding, a practice which is only recent in the breed and then only carried on by a small number of enthusiasts. Coolock Blackie won the milking trials at the Royal Show in 1948 and gave over 11,000 gallons at 4.9 percent butterfat. My present stock bull, Coolock Lord Nelson is out of a thousand-gallon dam and is grandson of Buckland June who holds the breed record at nearly 19,000 lb. of milk in a lactation. But what we really like, and what can be done under reasonable commercial conditions, is to have a herd of cows like my Bogardus Freesia who at twelve years old is still producing her steady 800–900 gallons each lactation. Recent successes in the show ring with my home-bred cattle include Barbacklow April who was a first prize heifer at the Dairy Show, and Barbacklow April who was first prize heifer at this year's Royal Show. Coolock Lord Nelson was second at the Royal Show, beaten only by that great show bull, Hookland Judge, who had three Royal Show wins to his credit.

The cow illustrated is Drumgauonagh Black Meg, a grand type of Kerry that won second prize at the Royal Show, 1947. She is nine years old and has had seven calves. Her first heifer (one of four in the herd) has given 7,197$\frac{1}{4}$ lb., 4.18 percent butterfat, in 361 days with her first calf. Black Meg's own best record is 10,364$\frac{3}{4}$ lb. in 360 days, fourth calf.

189

To quote the Kerry Society's official brochure: 'Nature's treatment has resulted in establishing a breed of cattle of unbeaten foraging capacity, and of iron constitution; a breed in which minor ailments are practically unknown and in which it is rare to meet one affected with tubercular troubles. The Kerry has been called "The Poor Man's Cow", and this she undoubtedly is, but she is the rich man's cow as well. The rich man tried her on account of her attractive appearance, and found that not only was her milk of the highest quality but that she could produce it economically, and was in fact a paying proposition. . . . The Kerry cow is in fact a profitable investment, as well as an ornament in every climate, on every class of soil, both for the large farmer, and the smallholder.'

How to Start

What is the best way to get started in Kerries? Well, your first step will be to find out what a good Kerry should look like. This is not a common breed and you may easily go wrong buying without previous knowledge of the breed. Read the points set out overleaf. Visit a number of herds whose names and addresses you can get from the Secretary of the Kerry Society, R.O. Hubl, Stanmore Hill, Middlesex. Go to any sale that may be held, but have an expert with you if possible. You could get a good view of the breed and an idea of prices at the Annual Show and Sale of Kerries held in Reading Cattle Market.

WHAT TO LOOK FOR IN A KERRY

The Cow

The cow should be long, level and deep; her colour black but a small amount of white on the udder and underline is permissible; her head long, clean cut and fine; her horns fine, mottled or white tipped with black, upright and cocked; her bone fine; her coat should be glossy and skin pliable; her udder should be soft and large but not fleshy, protruding well under the belly, the teats being placed square and well apart, the milk veins prominent and large; the tail should be long and well put on, a few white hairs are permissible in the tassel but the flag should not have a white appearance. The Kerry cow should not weigh over 1,000 lb. when in breeding condition.

The Bull

The bull should be black but a very small amount of white is permissible on or near the organs of generation; should have a long, clean-cut head, wide between the eyes; of masculine character, throat clean; horns medium length, mottled or white with black tips; withers fine, back level from withers to setting on of tail, which should be long, fine, tipped with black hairs, a few white hairs being permissible in the tassel but the flag should not have a white appearance. The Kerry Bull should not weigh over 1,250 lb. when in breeding condition.

Scale of Points

Kerry Cow

	points
General formation and character—Head, horns, and hair	30
Udder—Size, shape, situation of teats, milk veins and escutcheon, etc.	40
Quality of touch	10
Colour	20
Total	100

Kerry Bull

	points
General formation and character	25
Head, horns, and hair	25
Quality and touch	20
Colour	30
Total	100

BRITISH FRIESIANS
by B. J. HONEYSETT

In dealing with this subject, one feels that a few general remarks are essential. First of all, in a country such as ours with a climate and landscape varying from the sheltered and almost sub-tropical spots to be found in one or two parts of south Cornwall to the wild hill country of northern Scotland and again, from the high rainfall, low-lying lands of parts of the west to the dry, light soils of some of our eastern counties there is undoubtedly a place for each of our breeds of cattle.

39. The Kerry bull.

40. The Kerry cow.

41. The British Friesian bull.

42. The British Friesian cow.

To my mind, many farmers do not give enough consideration to the type of farm which they have, or are contemplating farming before choosing the breed of cattle they intend to keep, this is very important as although I know of a herd of British Friesians being kept on Dartmoor and others on high marginal land in Scotland, the land on which they are most at home, is the lush pasture of our low lands, whereas the reverse is probably true of some of our smaller dairy breeds.

The next point I would like to stress is that what is perhaps more important than the breed are the strains within the breed, as we all know that there are nearly as wide a difference in performance and type within a breed as there are between certain breeds.

Founding the Herd

When my brother and I took over the management of the dairy herd on this farm for our father in 1940, we decided that in place of the 'commercial Shorthorn type' cattle, we would found a pedigree herd, which would, we hoped, in time, build up to a carefully and closely bred herd of cattle from which bulls could go into other herds and stamp their progeny, as only the closely bred sires really will, but we had to decide first on a breed, and the one we finally chose after studying the main dairy breeds was the British Friesian, a choice which we have never regretted. Our main considerations were these: first of all, our farm of about two hundred acres was only from 50 ft. to 75 ft. above sea-level and also comprised about thirty acres in the Pevensey Marsh, which was valuable grazing land, on which we always run our heifers during the summer months (usually from March until the end of September). We were also anxious to bring our land into a high state of fertility and felt a large breed would suit our purpose best. Secondly, there was the future to consider, with two possibilities (quite likely probabilities) which seemed to stand out, one was that there was little doubt that the standard of living in this country was going to fall, and that in every country where that has already happened always the first food to have to forgo is meat, produced by the pure beef cattle, the supply having to be met as a by-product of the dairy herds, thus we felt that the British Friesian looked more like becoming the national dairy breed than any other, and I think the figures during the last few years have largely borne this out. The other possibility which we could not afford to overlook was that the day might come when milk would be paid for on a quality basis (some may say why then choose British Friesians), now don't forget what I wrote about the strains within the breeds, also that in the countries where milk is already paid for on a quality basis, Friesian cattle have held their own. In Holland there is of course qardly any other breed although milk has long been sold on the huality basis, the same applies to north-west Germany, and when we look at the U.S.A., we find the two leading breeds are still Friesians and Jerseys, perhaps New Zealand is an exception, where the Jersey breed is most favoured, but I think that is due to the climate and the fact that there have been good stocks of the breed in that country for many years.

We thus felt that in the British Friesian cow we had a good-sized animal capable of giving a large quantity of useful quality milk on a diet of largely home-produced bulky foods, one that could remain at pasture for a great part of the year, and whose bull calves would make useful beef if unwanted for breeding stock.

Having decided on our breed, the next question was the purchase of foundation stock, capital being strictly limited, it was not possible just to go to one of the leading herds and select what we fancied! However, we determined to find a bunch of females bred on similar lines, if possible by the same sire. After a number of unsuccessful enquiries we at last found a breeder (Mr. H. K. Keeling) who had been carefully building a herd for nearly thirty years, he had not purchased a female for twenty years and only used about six bulls during that time, in addition he had always given his cattle personal supervision, and full records had been kept. Although no attempt at close breeding had been practised, considerable care in choosing the herd sires had been exercised, the blood of the great Dutch bull Ceres had been freely used in the early days and further strengthened through a grandson of the celebrated Terling Marthus, R.M., later two introductions of the 1936 imported blood had been introduced through Warden Dutchman, R.M., and Royal Hiltkees 5th, the senior herd sire when the herd was dispersed, and already sire of over 200 daughters.

In connection with our purchase of foundation stock I would point out that this is one of the ways in which the various Breeders' Clubs and Associations can be of such value, as it was through the South Eastern British Friesian Breeders' Club that we first met our now esteemed friend Mr. Keeling. We eventually purchased eleven cows, all daughters of Egham Romulus R.M.P., R.M., a grandson of Terling Marthus, R.M., out of the twice 2,000 gallon R.M. cow, Egham Rue, whom Mr. Keeling had used in the herd for eight years, most of these cows were out of dams that were again half-sisters, thus we had a good beginning, as they were all pleasing animals, with good vessels, and having deep bodies on nice short legs, an additional advantage was that the cattle had never been forced in any way, mostly living on home-produced foods and always having an adequate supply of green stuff. These cows actually averaged over 1,600 gallons each with their first lactations on this farm, with seven already having qualified for their R.M., and three more that look like doing it during their present lactations. They have to date averaged over thirty tons of milk each and we hope that in time they will all obtain their R.M.L. (50 tons).

After two or three years, Mr. Keeling decided to retire, and thus arose the opportunity to purchase the daughters of our cows which were bred in his herd before we purchased them. So last summer, we sold twenty-seven of our own heifers, some commercial and some pedigree, but none of the Tunley cows, to make room (and raise funds!) for these daughters. I must mention here that we were not-interested in the daughters of Warden Dutchman R.M. only Royal Hiltkee 5th, as we did not consider Dutchman's daughters to have the right temperament (a very important feature in dairy cattle). Thus we purchased nine daughters by Royal Hiltkees 5th and two of his grand-daughters (these being by Tunley Hiltkees, our present senior stock bull) and mostly out of our own cows, an exception being the purchase of a daughter, grand-daughter and great-grand-daughter of a really good cow, Tunley Dairy Maid, two of them being full sisters to Tunley Hiltkees. Seven of these heifers have so far averaged 8,000 lb. at 3.98 percent butterfat in 230 days (all incomplete lactations) and still having an average daily output of 29 lb. and one second calver which has given 11,000 lb. at 4.2 percent butterfat still giving 25 lb. daily. Thus we already have three generations of some families and about thirty years' breeding.

Stock Bulls

To come to the stock bulls and breeding policy, we first purchased a bull with good milk and fat records but of no particular line of blood to use on the entire cross-bred herd; we kept this bull until he was eight years old and he sired some heavy milking cows. As soon as we had some pedigree cows we decided that our breeding policy should be to try to blend the blood of Terling Marthus with what we considered the best all-round bull of the 1936 importation, i.e. Royal Hiltkees R.M. (who already has twenty-five R.M. sons and fifty-seven R.M. daughters) thus trying to retain the great milking ability of the Marthus line and strengthening the butterfat through Royal Hiltkees. With this in mind, we purchased two bull calves out of heifers sold at the Terling and Lavenham Sale of 1947, one carrying eight and the other six crosses of Terling Marthus, and one of Royal Hiltkees;

these two bulls were used on half the herd each for two years, since when they have been largely rested until we have some of their daughters milking, which will be in the autumn when it is proposed to retain the best one for further use. Mr. Keeling had saved a son of Royal Hiltkees 5th, namely Tunley Hiltkees, out of one of his best families, the Petunias, and he promised us that when he had finished with him we should have the first offer, so after serving the heifers which were included in the sale he came to us, thus we have in him a continuation of the blood of the same two bulls, his dam being a great-grand-daughter of Terling Marthus and himself a grandson of Royal Hiltkees. We purchased the two full sisters to this bull in the sale for six hundred guineas, many considering them to be two of the best animals in the herd—the eldest had tested at 4.30 percent butterfat with her first calf, and will be about 4.20 percent butterfat with her second. The other one has not yet completed her first lactation but will give over 1,200 gallons at about 4 percent butterfat. The dam of this family is in the herd, Tunley Petunia 20th R.M.P., R.M., and gave almost 2,000 gallons on three-quarters last lactation (having lost one before we had her). She already has three R.M. yields, is a grand type of cow and her dam gave over 42 tons of milk at nearly 4 percent butterfat. We thus feel that this bull should leave some really good cattle—he has been used on ten of his dam's half-sisters, his two full sisters, five of his own half-sisters and two daughters, and the progeny from these matings look promising to date. We hope later to use him on the daughters of the other two bulls and vice versa, following with one of his sons out of his dam's half-sister, Tunley Edith 11th, a good cow who has already given three lactations of over 4 per cent butterfat and whose dam, now in calf with her fifteenth, and a wonderful wearing cow who already has four R.M. daughters and two more which look like becoming R.M.s in their present lactations. Therefore, we hope our future policy is already planned without having to go outside for new blood for some years.

Performance

Although the herd has not been going many years the herd average for the last three years has been over 1,300 gallons and led the East Sussex Branch N.M.R., for herd average and with the highest yielding cow. In 1950 the herd was placed third in the Royal Counties Show Dairy Herds Competition, open to all breeds in the County of Sussex, and at the last butterfat test, the entire herd averaged 4.09 percent; this, when the cows were on grass at the end of April. Bulls have been sold privately and at Reading for up to 380 guineas. Little showing has so far been done but when animals have gone out they have usually brought home cards with them. My own opinion of showing is that it is the shop window for the breeds and gives pleasure to those who like to see nice cattle, but has nothing to do with constructive breeding which can only be done in the office and on the farm.

Management

As mentioned earlier when starting the herd we were anxious to build up the farm to a high state of fertility as well as the cattle, it had, like many others, for various reasons been somewhat neglected during the period between the two wars. We have always considered the humus content of the soil to be very important, and made all the dung we possibly could, buying straw, as well as what we could grow on the farm. Another practice which we consider good is to keep the mower going over the pastures during the grazing season, thus keeping the grass young and allowing any 'heads' or coarse growth to be quickly returned as organic plant food to the soil in one of its most useful forms. On the question of spreading the droppings, we still have an open mind; there appear to be two schools of thought, one feeling that to spread is about one of the dirtiest habits on the farm, as the animals should be allowed to graze round them, going closer as the effect of the droppings dies away, whereas others take the line that unless you spread, a large amount of herbage is wasted and that any eggs, etc., are quickly destroyed by the sun. We are this year carefully spreading certain fields as the herd is taken out and watching results. Undoubtedly alternate grazing and cutting for silage is an excellent plan, so giving the field a rest and making full use of the extra fertility left by the animals.

The farm is mostly down to temporary grass, except a small acreage of good brookland pasture. We have tried a number of grass mixtures and have for the last few years been growing one consisting of Cocksfoot, Meadow Fescue, Tall Fescue, Meadow Foxtail grasses, with the addition of late-flowering Red Clover, Alsike, Chicory and Yarrow, we do not sow any White Clover, as we find on our soils this comes in on its own, so why spend money on seed? Ryegrass we dislike, as in our part of the country it is never there when you want it, the only time it seems to make any growth is early spring and late autumn, and as soon as it makes any stem, we have noticed the cattle dislike it, it is also a shallow-rooting plant, and a very poor humus builder. One plant which we have the greatest regard for is chicory; of all the herbs this to my mind seems to be the most valuable; from the cattle angle, it is very palatable, low in fibre, high in carbohydrates and being so deep-rooting it is drought-resisting and rich in minerals. We always sow 4 lb. per acre with all mixtures including lucerne, as we consider it an ideal companion for lucerne, helping to balance up the protein, it is also a great soil drainer, to the benefit of the future crops. I have often found its large tap root going down for three feet. We are this year putting down a small acreage of the Goosegreen mixture (minus the ryegrass) and shall be able to report later. I think that if farmers generally spent more time watching their cattle graze, particularly on natural herbage (growing on uncultivated ground) they would have a better understanding of what the cattle are likely to select, and what might with benefit be included in their wonderful looking straight leys!

About forty acres of dredge corn are grown for the dairy herd, pigs, and poultry, mostly sown in autumn and comprising oats, beans and a small percentage of wheat; this forms the main concentrate food during the winter, in addition a few acres of kale are grown and about six acres of market garden crops, the residue of which are also fed, such as the brussels sprouts plants after the best buttons have been sold, we also try to get as many catch crops as possible such as rape, turnips, and Italian ryegrass so as to maintain a supply of greenstuff almost throughout the year.

Milking is by machine. Regarding times of milking, we have tried doing it at the normal farm spacing, three times, and at twelve-hour intervals, and are satisfied that the last mentioned has most to recommend it, the thrice milking may be a little better for the udder in the case of a high-yielding cow, but against this you have the loss of rest, which is even more important, as unless the milking animals get proper rest periods they cannot utilize their food to the best advantage, it having been proved in the U.S.A. that when at grass, only about eight hours out of the twenty-four are spent collecting food, almost all the remainder being rest periods, unless disturbed; I think too that the butterfat will be found more consistent on the twelve-hours system. Two other points which we pay particular attention to during the winter months, when the cows are housed at night and during the day in very bad weather (although we always have them out for exercise each day) are daily grooming and clean mangers, the grooming is done thoroughly with a straight comb and a dandy brush and the mangers are washed out once a day and brushed out before each feed of concentrates.

The bulls are housed in comfortable pens with a four-foot return wall from the entrance, thus forming a warm corner which is kept strawed down. The exercise yards have tubular surrounds and are so placed that the bulls can see the cows come in and out for milking—an important point. Our senior stock bull is tethered out in the daytime most of the year, this is, of course, ideal, where they have the right temperament, but as any stock-man will know this is not always the case. The bulls are also kept groomed and given an occasional bath, which they seem to enjoy.

Up to the present the calves have been reared on the bucket, getting one gallon per day for the first three months, then gradually reducing it until they are weaned at $4\frac{1}{2}$ months, it is hoped later that when a cow obtains her R.M.L. (50 tons) that she will then be used for calf rearing, thus ensuring that she lives a natural life for the remainder of her days, and that if she breeds one good calf a year, she will still be a valuable asset to the herd.

As the farm is now being run entirely on the organic system, and no chemical fertilizers will in future be used, it is hoped that a continued improvement in health, production and hardiness will result, but a few years must pass before the full story can be told and seen.

In conclusion, I must say that this article has been written in odd moments during a very busy time so that full justice may not have been done to the subject but those who read it can be assured that it comes from the pen of one who is constantly in touch with his cattle and land. I am sure that whatever the breed the reader keeps or favours he will agree that as an enjoyable close to a busy day in this unsettled world there is no better sight than to watch a really good herd of British Friesians grazing a good pasture in the setting sun. One could almost imagine that the great Sir Walter Scott was thinking of such a scene, when he wrote the line, '*Shines Ebony and Ivory.*'

WHAT TO LOOK FOR IN THE FRIESIAN

The Bull

Head—Fairly large and distinctly masculine, broad near the horns, and tapering without undue length to nose, without Roman nose, the whole head being clean cut and without dewlap. The head should be carried high, to denote stylishness. The ears should be fairly large, thick, well set on, and carried evenly. The muzzle should be broad, with prominent nostrils.

Eyes—Large, bold, alert and set wide apart.

Horns—The horns should grow straight from the head, not too long, and turn inward and forward evenly, but not upward. They should not be coarse, but should be thick and white at the base, and gradually taper to a darker point.

Neck—Moderately long, thick, straight and deep, well let into the shoulders.

Shoulders—The shoulders should be strong, well laid in and broad at the points.

Body—Deep, with strong loin and well-sprung ribs, showing a good barrel with straight and parallel top and bottom outlines, freedom from hollows (particularly behind the shoulders) and with loose skin.

Quarters—Long and straight on top, hips level but not unduly wider than the pin bones, thighs wide and well let down, well fleshed outside down to the hocks. The buttocks should be wide and flat, without patches at the side of the tail-head.

Tail—The tail, the end of which must be white, should be set on level, in a line with the back, should not be coarse and should be carried in a perpendicular line to a point just behind and below the hocks.

Legs—The legs should be strong, straight and short, have nice but not too heavy bone, with good joints and feet, and should be placed well outside each corner of the body. The hocks should be clean, flat and broad.

Colours—Black and white are the only colours permissible. All four legs and the lower part of the tail should be white. The black-and-white markings should not be mottled or intermingled, and, except under special circumstances, a bull with a black hair spot on the foot or such spots on the feet is not eligible to have its entry registered.

The Cow

Head—Clean cut, distinctly feminine, and alert, wide at the horn, thin ears. The muzzle should be wide, and the whole head should not be too long.

Eyes—Clear, set wide apart, with gentle expression denoting docility.

Horns—The horns should grow straight from the head, should not be too long, and should turn inwards and forward evenly, but not upward. They should not be coarse, and should taper to a darker point.

Neck—Fairly long, straight and deep, and well laid into the shoulders.

Shoulders—The shoulders should be fairly strong, rather lean and well placed, broad at the points, and tapering to the withers.

Body—Deep, with strong and well-sprung ribs, showing a good barrel with straight and parallel top and bottom lines. Hollows (particularly behind the shoulders and front legs) should be avoided. The skin should be soft and pliable.

Quarters—Long, level and straight on top, with level hips and wide pelvic bones, and with good, deep thighs. The buttocks should be wide and flat, without patches at the side of the tail-head.

Udder—The udder should be capacious, thin and soft to the touch, showing prominently the milk veins, which should extend well forward under the body. The udder should be carried evenly and should extend well forward and come straight down behind, being well attached to the thighs. The twist should be wide and the teats of medium size, well and evenly placed underneath each corner of the udder.

Tail—The tail, the end of which must be white, should be set in level, in a line with the back, rather fine, and carried perpendicularly to a point just below and behind the hocks.

201

Legs—The legs should be strong, straight and short, having good but fine bone with good joints and feet, and placed well outside each corner of the body. The hocks should be clean, flat and broad.

Colours—Black and white are only colours permissible. All four legs and the lower part of the tail should be white. The black-and-white markings should not be mottled or intermingled.

DEXTERS

by LADY LODER

In 1908 I started Dexters by buying a dozen heifers from the late Duchess of Devonshire to stock a little 60-acre farm of *very* poor land. As I had to provide butter for the big house I found the Dexter the most suitable animal for this as being so hardy all they needed was an open shed in which to be milked, and they laid out all the year round, and the calves were reared in an open yard with a shelter roof at one end of it.

Butterfats were so good that in the summer we make 1 lb. of butter to every two gallons of milk, and I also won butter prizes competing against Jerseys.

I found I could keep five Dexters with the food required for three Jerseys, and when the artificial feeding problem became so difficult during the war, I gave up my Jersey herd, which I had kept on another farm for twelve years, and increased my Dexter herd as they were the most profitable animals on my poor land.

Dexters live to a great age and continue breeding well and still look quite fresh. Grinstead Dora 6th, the cow I took out to the Shows in 1949 and which won first and Champion at the Bath and West, Three Counties, Royal, Royal Counties and Sussex County shows, was ten years old and had had seven calves. Her average milk yield is 6,269 lb. with 4.06 per cent butterfat.

Milk Yields

In the National Milk Records for last year, Mr. Spencers' herd of Dexters in Kent, on better grassland, averaged 6,201 lb. for his cows, and 4,978 lb. for his heifers. Mrs. Wells, with Ickwell Amaryllis, had the highest yield for a single Dexter—9,629 lb. in 286 days with 4.79 per cent butterfat. My own Grinstead Trixie 9th had the best yield for three successive lactations:

6,099 lb. with 4.63 percent butterfat in 305 days with 3rd calf
6,315 lb. with 5.36 percent butterfat in 305 days with 4th calf
6,912 lb. with 4.89 percent butterfat in 305 days with 5th calf

A Dexter will yield between 500 and 600 gallons of milk without special feeding, but the following yields have been officially recorded, which by no means include all the yields.

Name of Cow	Age in Years	Yield in pounds	No. of days
Hookstile Titania 3324	10	12,747	365
Ashtonhayes Patricia 4166	5	12,122	365
Starlight of Grinstead 3511	9	11,505	365
Thorpe Dora 4337	7	11,341	364
Braxted Wendy 4286	7	11,136	365
Brokenhurst Penelope 3rd 3076	11	10,966	323
Grinstead Nightingale 3rd 3636	10	10,269	330
Ashtonhayes Portumna 4471	4	9,655	365
Grinstead Trixie 2nd 3977	4	9,592	362
Grinstead Hawk 5th 4108	6	9,518	351
Colomendy Marion 4188	7	9,477	354
Braxted Busy Bee 3928	7	9,441	342
Grinstead Dollie 2nd 4199	7	8,779	354
Nuthurst Hawk 3rd 3338	10	8,666	304
Beenham Dors 4632	6	7,763	329
Grinstead Lavender 6th 4597	4	7,114	314

Grinstead Taxus produced 433 lb. of butterfat in a year's lactation, representing an amount equal to her weight.

Origin

Dexter cattle were originally natives of the south and south-western districts of Ireland, where they have been bred by smallholders for some considerable time. They are a mountain breed and have roamed about the shelterless hillsides in an almost wild state of nature. The name 'Dexter' may have arisen from a gentleman of that name who was agent to Lord Hawarden and who conceived the idea of producing a little cow, suitable for both milking and fattening within the limits of his own farm on Valentia Island.

Dexters were first introduced into England in 1882, and shown at the Royal Show in Norwich in 1886. The English Dexter Herd Book was founded in 1900.

The Dexter is the smallest British breed, the cow averaging 650 lb. in weight, their smallness being accentuated by the shortness of their legs, between knee and fetlock.

Being a mountain breed they are extremely hardy and can with advantage be kept out of doors all the year round, even in the severest climates encountered in this country. This is particularly true on land likely to poach with heavier cattle, as due to their lighter weight, they can negotiate the worst gateways throughout the winter without undue troubles.

They are omnivorous in their grazing; they are capable of thriving on the closest grazed pasture where normally only sheep could make a living, whilst they will continually pick over coarse roughage, tackling such weeds as thistles and nettles, reducing the whole to an even cropped pasture. They are therefore ideal animals to keep where horses are kept extensively.

Considering their small size they are excellent milk yielders. The milk is of good quality, having a high butterfat content. What is more, the fats are in small globule form, while the curd is 'soft,' so that the milk is readily digested, making it pre-eminently suitable for children.

Dual Purpose

They are essentially dual purpose; steers develop rapidly, and are marketable between their second and third year. The flesh is thick, with the right amount of fat, whilst the joints are small, which meets the butchers' requirements.

They are regular breeders and reach maturity early, the first calf being produced at two years old. In spite of this, they live to a good age, eight calvings being the average, whilst fourteen offspring are not unknown. This low wastage in Dexter herds is of very great value.

They are extremely healthy, easily kept free from tuberculosis; and mastitis in its many forms is hardly known in a Dexter herd.

The maintenance ration of any animal varies according to its body weight. One accepted formula gives the relationship as two-thirds weight, from which it can be calculated that a 650-lb. Dexter takes roughly six-tenths of the food of a more normal animal of 1,300 lb. live weight. It therefore follows that ten Dexters can be maintained on the same area that supported, say, six animals of the larger breeds.

Over and above this maintenance figure, the ration required for milk can be taken as directly proportional; hence for equal milking efficiency the same ratio of ten to six holds good.

The result of being able to run more cows on a given acreage means that there are more frequent calvings, which by judicious management makes for a more level milk supply. Moreover, should a casualty occur in the herd, neither the loss in milk supply, nor capital value is so great.

For small farms a self-contained herd can be better justified; not only does the bull cost less to maintain, but the number of cows for which it is kept can be increased.

Roughage Users

Dexters are capable of converting roughage into useful food. Yields of up to two gallons a day can be maintained on hay alone; cake requirements are less, 3 lb. per gallon of milk above the first gallon being ample. For fattening also, very little cake is necessary if the animals have their fill of forage material.

Calves are easy and cheap to rear; six pints of milk per day is ample for their needs, and for the first three months only. They start to chew at a very early age, and good hay should be available from their third day.

A rough guide to milking efficiency is that a 650-lb. liveweight cow giving 500 gallons in a year is 25 percent efficient, whilst a similar cow giving 650 gallons would be 35 percent efficient. By comparison a 1,300-lb. cow, would be required to give 800 and 1,150 gallons respectively for similar efficiencies.

The appetite of a normal Dexter is 20 to 25 lb. of average hay per day.

Dexters have always been represented at the Smithfield Club Show of prize beef cattle, both in pure bred Dexter class of animals under three years old, and of small cross-bred cattle of under two years old, and in the pure-bred class animals average $6\frac{3}{4}$ cwt. have always fetched prices well above the average.

Good for Crossing

Dexters stamp their good qualities on any offspring, so that Dexter crosses also have good commercial value. This is particularly the case of using a Dexter bull in a beef herd where small early maturing animals are the result.

They have been exported to many parts of the world, including Argentina, Australia, Canada, India, Palestine, South Africa, and the United States, where in every case they have adapted themselves to the climate, and given satisfaction.

How to Make a Start

If you are interested to make a start in the Dexter breed you would find it is well to discuss the pros and cons with an established breeder, but first of all why not have a look at the breed at an agricultural show. Dexter cattle are exhibited at most of the larger Agricultural Shows, and pedigree Dexter herds are to be found in most milk-producing counties of England and Wales, the owners of which are usually very pleased to show their herds. Names of Dexter Breeders can be obtained from the the Dexter cattle breed associations (see appendix).

WHAT TO LOOK FOR IN A DEXTER

1. The Dexter is essentially both a milk-producing and a beef-making breed, and both these points should, in judging, be taken into consideration.
2. Colour—Bulls—Whole black or whole red (the two colours being of equal merit). A little white on organs of generation not to disqualify an animal which answers all other essentials of this standard description.

    Cows—Black or red, the two colours being of equal merit; a small amount of white on the udder and under-line is permissible (but not to extend beyond the navel), and also on the tassel of the tail.
3. Head and Neck—Head short and broad, with great width between the eyes and tapering gracefully towards muzzle, which should be large, with wide distended nostrils. Eyes bright, prominent, and a kind and placid expression.

    Neck—short, deep and thick, and well set into the shoulders, which, when viewed in front, should be wide, showing thickness through the heart, the breast coming well forward.

    Horns—These should be short and moderately thick, springing well from the head, with an inward and slightly upward curve.
4. Body—Shoulders of medium thickness, full and well filled in behind; hips wide; quarters thick and deep and well sprung, flat and wide across the loins, well ribbed up, straight under-line, udder well forward, and broad behind, with well-placed teats of moderate size, legs short (especially from knee to fetlock), strong, and well placed under body, which should be as close to the ground as possible. Tail well set on and level with back.
5. Skin—The skin should be soft and mellow, and handle well, not too thin, hair fine, plentiful and silky.

    Dexter bulls at three years old and over, should not exceed 900 lb. live weight, when in breeding condition, and younger bulls should weigh less in proportion.

    Dexter cows should not exceed 800 lb. live weight, when in breeding condition.

Scale of Points

Dexter Bulls

	points
General formation and character	25
Head, horns, and hair	25
Quality and touch	20
Colour*	30
Total	100

Dexter Cows

	points
Head, neck and horns	15
Body, top-line, under-line, ribs, setting on of tail, shortness of legs, etc.	25
Bag	40
Quality and touch	10
Colour*	10
Total	100

* White underneath forelegs and on brisket disqualify an animal.

RED POLLS

P. T. JOYCE, DORSET

It is now almost twenty years since I had to make up my mind which breed I should keep. It was at a time when the price of all agricultural produce was low and the margin of profit very small. A mistake almost certainly meant ruin. It was just about that time that the figures for the wastage of dairy cattle were first published, showing that an average cow lived in a herd, doing its job, for only two and a half years.

Bad times make good farmers, and every farmer has to use his own ingenuity. Mr. Hosier had set an example for those who lived on poor lands by treating cattle roughly and putting them through milking parlours instead of tying them up in a stall. It seemed to me then, and it has occurred to many others since, that cattle treated in this way must be hornless; and that cattle working for only two and a half years must make a useful carcass when they are killed. They must be cheap to rear and replace; they must give enough milk to make it worth while for two men to milk seventy. The herds which were making money for Mr. Hosier were averaging about 500 gallons of milk.

I did not start farming on the Hosier system, as I wished to give personal attention to the individual cattle which I started with. I purchased half my herd in the local market and half in the pedigree Red Poll market. I calved them down and milked them by hand in the traditional manner and found that the Red Polls averaged just over 800 gallons, rather better in fact than the Shorthorns. This left me no longer in doubt, although it was clear that I should have considerable difficulty in palming off useless animals, as I discovered them, by putting them into the local market. Red Polls were little appreciated in the west.

Since the revival of the beef industry, the dual purpose character of Red Poll cattle has been a very useful asset. I now rear every male and female on the cows which would otherwise have been discarded for the various reasons clearly set out by the statisticians twenty years ago. I have plenty of good cattle coming forward for beef which will fatten without concentrated food, and I am now in the position of having surplus breeding stock for sale.

After breeding dual-purpose cattle for twenty years, I realize that to have two objects in view is not so easy as having only one. But there are really many more than two objects. There is the animal's point of view, which is often ignored. Races of animals which have found environment uncongenial have died out, it seems, because they did not really wish to live in the new environment. We cannot ask a cow whether she prefers giving a very large quantity of milk, or whether she likes to get nice and fat once a year. We can only tell by the figures of longevity and breeding.

RED POLLS

by M. L. CULL, SOUTH WALES

In 1945 we took over three farms, all nearly derelict, the soil worn-out, the buildings inconvenient and dilapidated. Adequate stock was the first need and we were determined from the beginning that there should be a nucleus of pedigree stock on which we could build, until the farms had nothing except pedigree animals.

Milk for Cash and No Waste Calves

We therefore had to decide what kind of pedigree cattle we wanted and there were several factors to influence our choice. Firstly, it seemed essential that it should be a dairy herd as we needed a steady money return, no matter how small, to start coming in as quickly as possible. But, in view of the meat shortage, it seemed wasteful and uneconomic to keep a breed of cattle whose bull calves would be a sheer loss. Therefore it was necessary that it should be a dual-purpose breed.

There are not very many dual-purpose breeds from which to choose and everything seemed to point to Red Polls. Hardiness was important as all the farms are fairly high and very exposed. Also, at first there was very little accommodation for the cattle—and Red Polls are undoubtedly hardy.

Secondly we had decided that we wished to house our cattle in half-covered yards and for this the polled characteristic of the Red Polls was invaluable. Lastly there were already two or three herds in the district from which to obtain the nucleus of our breeding stock.

Improving the 'Cross-Breds'

So we bought a small bunch of in-calf heifers and later added some older cows and from these have built up a steadily increasing herd. We have never regretted our choice; the Red Polls completely satisfy us. So much so that we have started to use a Red Poll bull on our cross-bred beef cows, confident that while we are improving their milking quality we are in no way spoiling their capacity for beef. The Red Poll milks well; from 800 to 1,000 gallons are usual for a mature cow while records up to 2,000 are not unknown. Their butterfat is good, though, of course, it cannot compare with the Channel Island breeds. We have as yet no personal experience of their beefing capabilities but the records of many herds, all over the country, prove that it is quite usual to rear bullocks that will grade as A+ or Super Special out of 1,000-gallon dams. The Red Poll is slow maturing but is very long lived, keeping up her milk production to the end. She is also an extremely healthy animal.

Rearing Methods

We are in no position to talk of our 'methods of animal husbandry,' for we have not had the herd sufficiently long to have evolved any methods particularly our own. All we do is to attempt to do our best for our animals and adapt to our own conditions the accepted methods of herd management.

Thus the calf is left to suckle the cow for the first four days of its life and is then bucket fed on whole milk. All the calves are given sufficient whole milk to ensure a really good start, but the bull calves destined to be reared as steers are transferred to a gruel after some weeks. This is done in order

43. The Dexter bull.

44. The Dexter cow.

45. The Red Poll bull.

46. The Red Poll cow.

to economize milk and is not perhaps an ideal practice, but the steers seem to do very well despite it. From about nine months old, until they calve down, the heifers are out all the time. They are served at approximately two years and thus calve just before three years old.

Home-Grown Foods

The cows are hand milked and are fed as far as possible on home-grown foods. The bulk foods are hay, oat straw and silage made from oats and vetches, lucerne or whatever else we can muster. Marrow stem kale is grown for feed in the autumn and early winter and a small amount of mangolds also which are used as a reserve. The concentrates consist to a great extent of oatmeal and linseed meal. The linseed is always home-grown and is ground in a hammer mill on the farm, thus the oil is also fed.

The new leys which are now beginning to supply the greater part of the grazing are based on the Clifton Park mixtures and adapted to our soil and needs. For example, we cut down to a minimum the amount of yarrow in the mixtures, for yarrow occurs naturally in our pastures. The same thing is done with chicory, for this grows so vigorously here that it tends to crowd out some of the other plants. Also on one of the farms perennial ryegrass does not do very well, for it suffers very badly during dry spells and there cocksfoot is made the basis of the leys instead.

No attempts are made to force milk yields or growth. The cows are milked twice a day, and are fed before calving merely to ensure adequate nutriment for both cow and calf. We do not approve of pre-milking as a rule but practise it if the cow is badly congested and is obviously in discomfort. We keep natural methods as our ideal, and have had a number of successes in the natural treatment of troubles like sterility and mastitis on rare occasions that they have arisen.

In everything the greatest care is taken to treat the cattle with quietness and consideration, to treat them as living creatures, not machines.

WHAT TO LOOK FOR IN A RED POLL

The Breed Standard Description

The Red Poll is a dual-purpose animal, the breed was evolved to combine the production of the very highest standard of beef with a satisfactory milk yield. Accordingly judging should aim at deciding the best combination of these qualities. Moreover an obvious deficiency in one cannot be counterbalanced by superlative excellence in the other.

Colour—Red, but white on the udder or the end of the tail is permissible.

Head—The head must be polled.

Nose—The nose should be flesh-coloured. Should it be blue or black, this constitutes a disqualification.

The Cow

The cow should have a fine head and neck.

Her back should be level, with the tail long and thin and set on level with it.

Her loin should be wide and her hips evenly rounded and not too prominent.

Her body should be deep, with ribs well sprung, the legs being at the four corners and set well apart. She should be a good mover on short legs.

Her hindquarters should be long from hip to aitch-bone and not patchy at the rump ends, the buttocks being deep and well-fleshed down to the hock.

Her forearms and half-legs should be well developed.

She should be thick through the heart and her brisket should be deep, wide and forward.

Her skin should be fine and soft to the touch.

Her udder should be well developed but not pendulous and should come well up between the hind legs, and run well forward.

The teats should be of moderate size set evenly at the four lower corners of the udder and pointing to the ground.

The milk veins should run well forward along the belly.

The Bull

A similar description to that given for a cow applies to a bull; except for the reference to the head and neck, and to the udder.

A bull should be a decidedly masculine type with a strong head and neck, a powerful chest and well-developed rudimentary teats.

He should be a good over on short legs and his testicles should be flesh coloured and hang evenly.

Any white patch is a disqualification; any white hairs other than on the tip of the tail, constitute a fault.

AYRSHIRES

by S. MAYALL

I started milk production in 1923 with a mixed herd, mainly non-pedigree Shorthorns. It was two years later at the Dairy Show that I had my first introduction to Ayrshires and was greatly impressed by their dairy-like qualities. This was the year when the championship was won by that great cow Millantae Mayflower. A few years later I was in need of some tuberculin-tested heifers for autumn calving; I made my first trip to Scotland and came back with two truckloads. The next year's experience with these confirmed me in a love for the Ayrshire which has increased with time and today I own over 300 and another 200 in a partnership.

Why?

What a lovely animal the Ayrshire cow is with her graceful horns carried so proudly on a fine head; what other breed has that style and carriage? She has a straight back, fine horns and an udder that is the envy of all with its great capacity and perfect shape, coming right forward under the belly to complete the under-line and sweeping out behind and well up. The beauty of Ayrshires has done much to attract new breeders (for the last three years new members have joined the Herd Book Society at the rate of three a day) but in the long run a breed must stand or fall on its commercial qualities and herein the Ayrshire also excels.

We often hear it said that there are too many breeds of cattle in this country and though at first sight it may seem to be so, it must be remembered that we have very diverse conditions in different districts and that the various breeds have been developed as being especially suitable for the conditions of their native district. The Ayrshire comes from the south-west of Scotland, mostly high-lying land, much of it poor, exposed to the elements and requiring stock which is hardy and able to stand adverse conditions and yet able to give a generous supply of rich milk. From these beginnings has been built up a breed of reasonable size, with a low maintenance requirement, very economical in food conversion and a clean grazer.

Milk was mainly used in Scotland for cheese production and the cattle were bred to give milk especially suitable for this purpose with the smallest fat globules of any breed. This has its advantage to-day when most milk goes for liquid consumption and it is believed that the small fat globules makes Ayrshire milk the most digestible of all for children.

What I Want from Ayrshires

Management of the herd falls into two parts, long-term planning including breeding and day-to-day management. In this we have never sought herd record yields as they can only be attained by methods which are bound to react unfavourably on the health and well-being of the herd. A calf every year, steady milk production and a long working life are what is wanted. No herd improvement is likely when culling has to be done at the dictate of disease and infirmity and when all the heifers born are required for herd replacement; I can truthfully say that this herd has made great strides towards our ideal since I reached the position of not having to take into the herd each year more than 50 percent of the heifers reared.

The aim has been 1,000 gallons at 4 percent butterfat for the third-calf cow and this aim has very nearly been achieved in the last two years over which period the cows of two lactations upwards have averaged just over 1,000 gallons at 3.9 per cent butterfat.

At the same time I believe that we must not neglect type though there are many breeders to-day who believe that performance is all that matters. In considering type it is not easy to decide which points have economic importance and which are purely fancy, but twenty years ago I fixed in my mind the picture of the Ayrshire cow that I wanted and took great trouble to find a strain which could be line-bred to produce her. The first principal herd sire was Bargower Rehearsal 45291 whose dam was Bargower Silver Bell 18th. When Silver Bell 18th was at her prime I regarded her as the perfect Ayrshire cow. She was a Supreme Champion of the Highland Show and gave:

1,024 gallons at 4.29 percent
1,237 gallons at 3.86 percent
1,314 gallons at 4.51 percent
1,233 gallons at 4.60 percent

The ability to stand a long and useful life is a point to watch in breeding. The dam of another sire, Bargower Home Pride, Bargower Silver Bell 17th; lived to be seventeen, having given over 10,000 gallons of milk at over 4 percent butterfat (part unofficial records). The dam of the sire of this bull also lived to seventeen years, so I hope that the daughters now calving will prove to be long-wearing. That some success has been achieved in regular breeding and long life can be seen from the photograph of Pimhill Sarah heading a line of five generations see plate 2. At the time when the picture was taken she and all her descendants had completed twenty-three lactations in the herd, averaging 1,158 gallons.

How We Get It

The central feature of the management of the herd is the organic farming of the land which contributes 95 percent of the food required in the form of organically grown crops. The balance of food which is bought consists almost entirely of fish meal, beans, bran, beet pulp and seaweed meal. Except for a few outlying fields the land is under a six-course rotation, winter corn, roots or silage, spring corn followed by three years' ley containing deep-rooting species and herbs. The corn is nearly all dredge corn, a mixture of wheat, oats, barley and beans for stock feeding. A large amount of compost is made and all manure goes through the heaps, including that from 250 to 300 pigs; no artificial manures are used. Grass is preserved by both drying and the making of silage, both pit and stack. Grazing is controlled by electric fences. In winter the dried grass and silage provide maintenance and $1\frac{1}{2}$ gallons of milk. The remainder of the production ration coming from the home-grown dredge corn with the addition of the bought foods mentioned above. After Christmas a very small quantity of mangold or fodder beet is given; the amount is too small to affect the ration but it adds to the variety of food and the cows look eagerly for it.

Milk is bottled on the farm for sale to a retailer and so it is important to maintain a reasonably level supply throughout the year. For this reason the first heifers are calved down about the middle of July and they continue through to mid-November by which time there is only a stray one or two left. The cows start in September and carry on through the winter until March. I like to calve down the heifers at between twenty-seven and thirty-three months as far as this is possible and they are never pushed for production before or after calving. The present-day custom of evaluating a bull by the first lactations of his daughters, whilst giving the earliest possible knowledge of the bull which is in itself desirable, does tend, I am sure, to encourage breeders to force their stock for high yield at an age when they are least fitted to stand it with unfortunate results on productivity and wearing qualities later in life.

Finally a word on the bulls; three things are regarded as of major importance in management—exercise, feeding and interest. Exercise may be provided by daily walks, by tethering out or at least by provision of an exercise yard attached to the bull house. In feeding, the ideal for bulls is little and good; too much bulk makes him lazy and slow to serve; before and during a season of heavy service my bulls receive $\frac{1}{2}$ lb. fish meal and $\frac{1}{4}$ lb. seaweed meal or cubes as part of their daily ration. By interest I mean that the bull-pen should be so situated that the bull can see out freely and so have some interest throughout the day; it is best of all if he can see the cows pass by at milking time. Nothing is so conducive to bad temper as solitary confinement. Regular quiet handling is also a part of the routine.

A good herd is a man's livelihood and hobby rolled into one, and what if we do have a few disappointments, there are always the bulling heifers coming along. We count our progress with thankfulness, certain that next year we shall show the world! My Ayrshires have taught me much and given me many happy hours in the learning.

WHAT TO LOOK FOR IN AN AYRSHIRE

The Bull

Head	*points*
Forehead—Broad and clearly defined	2
Horns—Fine at base, set wide apart inclining upwards	1
Face—Of medium length, clean cut, showing facial veins	2
Muzzle—Broad and strong without coarseness	2
Nostrils—Large and open	2
Jaws—Wide at the base and strong, meeting evenly	1
Eyes—Moderately large, full and bright	2
Ears—Of medium size and bright, carried alert	1
Expression—Full of vigour, resolution, and masculinity	2
	15

Neck

Of medium length, somewhat arched, large and strong in the muscles on top, inclined to flatness on sides, enlarging symmetrically towards the shoulders, throat clean and free from loose skin	4
	4

Fore Quarters

Shoulders—Strong, smoothly blending into body with good distance through from point to point and fine on top	3
Chest—Low, deep and full between and back of fore legs	5
Brisket—Not too prominent, and with very little dewlap	2
Legs and Feet—Legs well apart, straight and short, shanks fine and smooth, joints firm, feet of medium size, round, solid and deep	2
	12

217

Body   *points*

Back—Short and straight, chine strongly developed and open
    jointed   5
Loin—Broad, strong and level   4
Ribs—Long, broad, strong, well sprung and wide apart   4
Abdomen—Large and deep, trimly held up with muscular
    development   4
Flank—Thin and arching   1

                                             18

Hind Quarters

Rump—Well set in, level and long from hooks to pin bones   2
Hooks—Medium distance apart, proportionately narrower
    than in female, not rising above the level of the back   2
Pin Bones—High, wide apart   3
Pelvic Bones—Wide   2
Tail—Fine, long and set on a level with back   1

                                           10

Thighs, Legs and Feet

Thighs—Medium, long and wide apart
  points
Legs—Straight, set well apart, hocks wide apart, point of
    hocks not to incline towards each other, shank fine and
    smooth
Feet—Medium size, round, solid, and deep, not to cross in
    walking   16

                                           16

Scrotum

Well developed and strongly carried. Rudimentaries, veins, etc. Teats
    of uniform size squarely placed wide apart and free from scrotum;
    veins long, large, tortuous with extensions entering large orifice   2

                                         2

Colour

Red of any shade, brown or these with white, mahogany and white,
    black and white, or white; each colour distinctly defined   2

                                       2

Covering	points
Skin—Medium thickness, mellow and elastic	4
Hair—Soft and fine	2
	6

Character	points
Carriage—General appearance and style active, vigorous, showing strong masculine character; temperament, mild	10
	10

Weight	
At maturity, from 1,500 lb. upwards	5
	5

	Total 100

The Cow

Head	points
Forehead—Broad and clearly defined	2
Horns—Wide set on and inclining upwards	1
Face—Of medium length, slightly dished, clean cut, showing veins	2
Muzzle—Broad and strong, without coarseness, nostrils large	2
Jaws—Wide at the base and strong, meeting evenly	2
Eyes—Full and bright, with placid expression	2
Ears—Of medium size and fine, carried alert	1
	12

An animal which has been cleanly and neatly dehorned, and whose head shows true Ayrshire character, shall not be penalized.

Neck	
Fine throughout, throat clean, neatly joined to head and shoulders, of good length, moderately thin, nearly free from loose skin, elegant in bearing	3
	3

Fore Quarters	
Shoulders—Light, good distance through from point to point but sharp at withers, smoothly blending into body	2
Chest—Low, deep and full between and back of forelegs	2
Brisket—Light	1

Legs and Feet—Legs straight and short, well apart, shanks fine *points*
  and smooth, joints firm. Feet medium size, round, solid and deep 2

  7

Body

Back—Strong and straight, chine lean, sharp and open jointed 4
Loin—Broad, strong and level 2
Ribs—Long, broad, wide apart and well sprung 4
Abdomen—Capacious, deep firmly held up with strong
  muscular development 3
Flank—Thin and arching 2

  15

Hind Quarters

Rump—Well set in, wide, level and long from hooks to pin bones,
  a reasonable pelvic arch allowed 2
Hooks—Wide apart and not projecting above back nor unduly
  overlaid with fat 1
Pin Bones—High and wide apart 2
Pelvic Bones—Wide 2
Tail—Long, fine, set on a level with back 1

  8

Thighs, Legs and Feet

Thighs—Medium, short and wide apart
Legs—Strong, short, straight when viewed from behind and set well apart;
  hocks wide apart, point of hocks not to incline towards each other,
  shanks fine and smooth, joints firm.
Feet—Medium size round, solid, and deep, not to cross in walking 15

  15

Udder

Long, wide, deep, but not pendulous, nor fleshy; firmly attached to the body,
  extending well up behind and far forward; quarters even; sole nearly
  level and not excessively indented between teats, udder veins well
  developed and plainly visible 15

  15

	points
Teats	
Evenly placed, distance apart from side to side equal to half the breadth of udder, from back to front equal to one-third of the length; length $2\frac{1}{2}$ to $3\frac{1}{2}$ inches, and not less than 2 inches, thickness in keeping with length, hanging perpendicularly and slightly tapering, and free flow of milk when pressed	5
	5
Mammary Veins	
Large, long, tortuous, branching and entering large orifices	5
	5
Colour	
Red of any shade, brown or these with white, mahogany and white, black and white, or white; each colour distinctly defined	1
	1
Covering	
Skin—Of medium thickness, mellow and elastic	3
Hair—Soft and fine	2
	5
Character	
Carriage—General appearance and style; alert, vigorous, showing strong character; temperament, mild	5
	5
Weight	
At maturity, from 1,000 lb. upwards	4
	4
Total	100

SOUTH DEVONS

by George Eustace

When I started at Tregotha, Hayle, in west Cornwall, I wished to devote my main energies to spring cabbage, broccoli, and early potatoes as the land and climate were ideal for these. In order to support this policy I wanted a breed of cattle which were hardy and did not need pampering; which could give me an economic milk yield of a high butterfat, and which could produce steers for yarding. I chose South Devons and have never regretted that decision. My family has bred South Devons for more than half a century.

Why?

While arriving at this decision I examined the past history of the breed and was impressed more by the potentials the breed had to offer than by its past history. South Devons had been used mainly by tenant farmers for centuries, and no constructive breeding had been done, neither had any rich people attempted to improve the breed above the general level.

The only improvement came from the general farmer in his own way, by rearing a bull from his own best cream and butter cows. The farmer's relations or neighbours would probably know his herd as well as he did himself and would buy or ask for a bull out of a certain cow. In that way the slow but steady improvement in the breed must have taken place, and I assume that during that span of time the farmer's income was derived mainly from cream and butter as ready cash and store and fat cattle with which to pay the rent.

Milk Yields

Little emphasis or importance was placed on milk yields, except by the producer retailers who lived close to the towns and kept 'flying' herds. They came into the local markets and bought the best milking and uddered South Devon cows, and after milking them for one lactation then graded them out. In this way such farmers must have got through from between 300 and 500 potential thousand gallon cows each year, and their breeding value was therefore completely lost to the breed. As an example of this the Supreme Champion cow at the London Dairy Show in 1930 was saved from that fate by the well-known breeder Mr. George Wills who outbid a dairyman and got her for £42 at Totnes Market. Against this background I found herds averaging over 900 gallons—and some over 1,000 gallons; I found South Devon cows walking away with the Supreme Championship

222

at the London Milking Trials; and I found a very great demand for the South Devon steers by the Midland graziers and feeders. In fact when I chose South Devons fifteen years ago I decided they possessed collectively those attributes, each of which other breeds were attempting to acquire individually in their own cattle.

Outstanding Improvements

Since I commenced with South Devons the breed has improved considerably, although it is only in the past few years that the general farmer has started to support this improvement policy. Other breeds have to breed for improvement, which is a long-term policy, but South Devon owners need only improve their management in the first instance in order to obtain a greater return from their cattle. My own neighbours, the Lello Brothers, placed their herd in charge of a good cowman at the end of February 1948, and their milk sales in March and April over the last four years were:

	1946–7	*1947–8*	*1948–9*	*1949–50*
March	511	894	1,213	1,587
April	581	1,155	1,280	1,762

These production figures were obtained from the same cows, and in the last year the herd has been increased by the addition of two home-bred heifers.

Mr. R. W. Darke, of Kingsbridge, in Devon, also changed his management, and placed his herd in charge of a good cowman at the end of 1947, and obtained the following herd averages:

1946	*1947*	*1948*	*1949*
$7,662\frac{1}{2}$ lb.	$7,801\frac{1}{2}$ lb.	$10,963\frac{3}{4}$	10,249 lb.

Again these figures resulted from the same number of cows, and no new cows were bought in to replace poor milkers.

These are only two examples of what can be done to the breed by management. On the other hand Mr. C. Nielsen of Devonshire has shown what can be done by breeding together with good management. He has been line-breeding and his first batch of heifers have just finished their first lactations averaging 1,160 gallons at 4.58 percent butterfat. Such performances place South Devons right in the top of the pure dairy breeds, and this without counting the added asset of first class beef stores, and 4d. per gallon extra which some breeders are now able to get for their quality milk.

47. The Ayrshire bull.

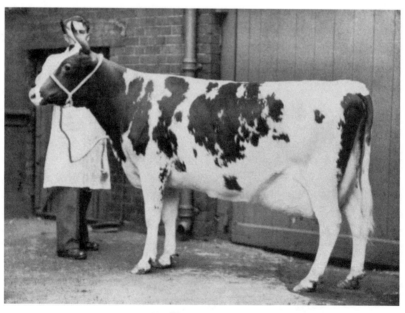

48. The Ayrshire cow.

49. The South Devon bull.

50. The South Devon cow.

How?

My own farm is only 82 acres of medium loam and it is split into the following:

> 17 acres of broccoli
> 25 acres corn
> 8 acres potatoes
> 8 acres spring cabbage
> 3 acres mangolds
> 30 acres grass

I take two crops a year from some fields, for instance, I plant my potatoes at the end of April and harvest them in June when I then plant broccoli, which I finish cutting by the beginning of April.

Most of my corn is dredge. My usual rotation is ley, broccoli, corn, spring cabbage, broccoli and then to corn undersown.

I keep 55 South Devons on this small intensive farm, which rather discounts the adverse criticism that they require unlimited grazing. I have fifteen cows and followers and shall feed out about eight good steers.

Beefing Qualities

I recently graded two at £79 each, which weighed nearly 14 cwt. at under three years and were given 'Special.' Another I graded weighed $17\frac{3}{4}$ cwt. at two years nine months, was given 'Special' and for which I received £102. This had been to the Fat Stock Shows and therefore had received slightly better treatment than the others but he did show what can be done by a little extra feeding in addition to grazing.

My herd average last year was 583 gallons for seven cows which included two which had been transferred as nurse cows after giving less than 200 gallons. My heifers averaged 7,031 lb. 'Tregotha Daisy' has just given $9,142\frac{1}{2}$ lb. in 310 days with 4.63 percent butterfat on eight tests. 'Tregotha Rose 4th' has just given as a heifer $9,852\frac{1}{2}$ lb. in 365 days, and she gave four gallons at the London Dairy Show in 1949. Another heifer, 'Tregotha Gem 3rd' has just finished with $7,235\frac{1}{4}$ lb. in 309 days at 4.49 percent over seven tests.

My herd is not treated as a dairy herd, and I use quite a number of my cows as nurse cows in order to rear many calves. These nurse cows are taken out of my milking herd as and when required quite irrespective of type or milk yields, which is a practice not conducive to high herd averages. In the past I have done this in order to rear as many calves as possible as they trample a lot of muck and this is required for my other activities.

226

I have decided, however, to follow the example of many of my fellow breeders and to manage my cows in keeping with higher milk yields. I am hoping my next year's average will then be between 800 and 900 gallons.

In 1947 I exhibited at the London Dairy Show and won first for Heifer Inspection and third in the Milking Trials. In 1948 I won two first prizes for Inspection and a second in the Milking Trials, and in 1949 I won two second prizes for Inspection and a third in the Milking Trials. At the 1950 Devon County Show I won the *Western Morning News* Challenge Cup for the best dairy cow. My herd has been attested since 1946 and we have never had even a doubtful reactor, inclusive of the initial tests.

My South Devons have played their part wonderfully well, and this in spite of the fact that they have always taken second place to my other farming activities in respect of their milk production. But I have always been careful with my breeding and type, and therefore know that I have the material with which to achieve a 900-gallon herd average. One of the misfortunes of this breed is that they are so docile and hardy and require so little pampering that they are too often left to carry on themselves. Even then they do a good job and in 1949 the official herd averages were only just below 700 gallons.

With decent treatment or in the hands of dairy farmers this average could easily go to at least 800 gallons after one year of management for milk production.

WHAT TO LOOK FOR IN A SOUTH DEVON

Scale of Points

Cow

General Appearance	*points*
1. General Symmetry, wide, deep, well-balanced with good lines. Colour—medium red	10
2. Evenness of flesh, quality, hide of moderate thickness, loose and mellow to the touch	7
	17

Head	
3. Head, feminine, clear cut (face not narrow) and of medium length; eyes full; nose flesh colour, with wide expansive nostrils; ears of medium size	4
4. Horns, white or yellow, not coarse, slightly forward and drooping	2
	6

	points
Neck	
5. Fine but strong, fairly long, clear at junction with head	2
	2
Fore Quarters	
6. Shoulders, covered at the points, medium distance through from point to point, neat on top, smoothly blended into body	3
	3
Body	
7. Chest, deep, wide between and behind forelegs, no depression behind shoulder blades	3
8. Back, level with loin, strong and wide	3
9. Ribs, deep, carried well back, nicely sprung, giving a capacious barrel,	4
	10
Hind Quarters	
10. Hips, fairly wide, but not prominent	2
11. Rounds, medium	2
12. Rump, wide, long and level. Tail neatly and evenly set in and of good length	4
	8
Legs and Feet	
13. Well apart, short; shanks fine and clean, feet good	4
	4
Milk Vessel	
14. Udder, skin thin, soft and elastic, hair fine and silky; udder long, wide and deep, extending well up behind and far forward, quarters even and fleshy	26
15. Teats of medium size, evenly placed, well set and uniform	15
16. Milk veins, prominent and well developed and large milk wells	9
	50
Total	100

Scale of Points

Bull

General Appearance

1. Straight top, good underline, deep short legs, symmetrical	10
2. Hide medium, mellow, pliable. Hair medium red, soft and curly, even fleshed	6
3. Alert, active. Forceful action, head and ears well carried, good 'character' generally	4
	20

Conformation

4. Head—broad, medium length, eyes full, nose white, horns yellow or white, ears medium size. Neck, medium length	10 10
5. Legs—short and straight, wide apart; chest full, wide and deep. Girth large and full, shoulders not too heavy	10
6. Back—straight, loin broad, level and thick	16
7. Barrel—broad, deep, capacious. Ribs long, well back and well sprung and even fleshed. Flanks full, even with under-line	12
8. Hips—smoothly covered, width in proportion to other parts. Rump medium length, wide and level. Rounds deep. Legs squarely placed straight and short	8
9. Sound testicles, long and good size 'teats' and squarely placed. Tail well placed and long with good brush	8
10. Rich medium red in colour, soft curly hair, hide medium, loose and mellow	6
Total	100

Appendix 3

THE COMPOSITION OF THE MILK

The chemical constituents of milk are: water, butterfat, albuminoids (including casein and albumin), milk sugar and ash or mineral matter. For legal and other purposes the composition of milk is usually stated as fat, solids not fat, total solids, and water. The solids not fat include the albuminoids, ash and sugar, and the total solids everything except water. The minimum legal requirements are 3 percent fat and 8.5 percent solids not fat; when milk falls below this standard it is presumed at law to be adulterated until the contrary is proved.

COMPOSITION OF VARIOUS MILKS

	Fat	Albumin-oids	Milk Sugar	Ash	Water
Cow (average)	3.73	3.58	4.90	0.71	87.08
Human	3.78	2.29	6.21	0.31	87.41
Goat	4.78	4.29	4.46	0.76	85.71
Ewe	6.86	6.52	4.91	0.89	80.82
Mare	1.20	2.00	5.70	0.40	90.70
Sow	4.55	7.23	3.13	1.05	84.04
Colostrum	3.40	20.70	2.50	1.80	71.70
Medium Cream	36.20	6.00	2.50	0.30	55.00
Devonshire Cream	67.50	4.90	1.00	0.50	26.10
Separated Milk	0.20	3.30	5.10	0.60	90.80
Buttermilk	0.50	3.60	4.06	0.75	90.39

COMPOSITION OF FIRST AND LAST MILK

	Fat	Albumin-oids	Total Solids	Water
First quart drawn	1.20	3.70	10.58	89.42
Last quart drawn	7.88	3.48	16.63	83.37
Strippings	10.00	3.37	19.40	80.60

Appendix 4

HOW TO ESTIMATE CONTENTS OF STACKS, SILOS, CLAMPS AND DUTCH BARNS

1. (*a*) If rectangular, multiply length by breadth by height
   (*b*) If circular, multiply circumference by itself and by .08 and then by height.
   (*c*) If prism, multiply length by breadth at base and then by half the height.
   (*d*) If cone, multiply circumference at based by itself and by .08 and then by one-third the perpendicular height.

Estimating Stack Weights

2. Add (*a*) and (*c*) or (*b*) and (*d*) together: result will be contents in cubic feet if measurements taken in feet.

3. Reduce to cubic yards by dividing by 27.

4. Reduce to tons by dividing by one of the following numbers according to the shape and condition of the stack:

Hay Weights

Number of cubic yards per ton

	Rectangular	*Round*
If not settled	12	13
If compact	8	9

Straw

Number of cubic yards per ton:
Wheat 18–20   Oats 20–23   Barley 20–23

Roots

Weight per cubic foot in clamp:

Turnips 33 lb.	Mangolds 35 lb.	Carrots 31 lb.
Swedes 34 lb.	Potatoes 42 lb.	Parsnips 31 lb.

231

Compost

1 cubic yard of compost weighs 12 to 16 cwt. or 1 ton of compost bulks 1¼ to 1⅜ cubic yards, when mature.

Silos

A silo 15 feet diameter and 30 feet high (5,300 cubic feet) holds 100 tons of silage, the yield of 6 acres maize, 10 acres of oats and vetches, 13 acres of clover ley, 20 acres meadow grass, 12 acres sainfoin or lucerne.

A silo 12 feet diameter and 24 feet high has half the above capacity.

1 cubic yard of finished silage weighs approximately 1 ton.

Appendix 5: Resources

Below are updated contact points mentioned by N. Turner that are still in existence today. The avid student will no doubt turn up additional sources.

The Soil Association, South Plaza, Marlborough Street, Bristol BS1 3NX, United Kingdom, phone 0117-314-5000, website *www.soilassociation.org.*

Cotswold Seed Ltd. [Herbal Ley Seed Distributor], Cotswold Business Village, Moreton-in-Marsh, Gloucestershire GL56 0JQ, United Kingdom, website *www.cotswoldseeds.co.uk/ herballeys.htm.*

ANIMAL HEALTH ASSOCIATIONS

United States Animal Health Association, P.O. Box 8805, St Joseph, Missouri 64508, phone 816-671-1144, website *www. usaha.org.*

Institute for Animal Health, Compton Laboratory, Compton, Newbury, Berks RG20 7NN, United Kingdom, website *www. iah.bbsrc.ac.uk.*

New Zealand Association for Animal Health and Crop Protection, P.O. Box 5069, Wellington, New Zealand, website *www1.agcarm.co.nz.*

Animal Health Alliance Ltd., Level 2, AMP Building, 1 Hobart Place, Canberra, ACT 2601, Australia, website *www. animalhealthalliance.org.au.*

DEXTER CATTLE SOCIETIES

American Dexter Cattle Association, 4150 Merino Avenue, Watertown, Minnesota 55388, phone 952-215-2206, website *www.dextercattle.org.*

The Dexter Cattle Society, 1st Floor, RASE Offices, Stoneleigh Park, Warks CV8 2LZ, United Kingdom, phone 0247-669-2300, website *www. dextercattle.co.uk.*

Dexter Cattle Society New Zealand, 92A Takanini-Clevedon Road, Ardmore, RD 2, Papakura, Aukland, New Zealand, website *www.dexter-cattle.co.nz.*

Dexters—Beefy Little Milkers, ABRI—University of New England, Armidale, NSW 2351, Australia, website *dexter.une. edu.au.*

Index

INDEX

Also by Newman Turner

Fertility Pastures
by Newman Turner

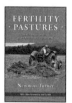

In *Fertility Pastures*, Turner details his methods of intensive pasture-based production of beef and dairy cows in a practical guide to profitable, labor-saving livestock production. He developed a system of complex "herbal ley mixtures," or blends of pasture grasses and herbs, with each ingredient chosen to perform an essential function in providing a specific nutrient to the animal or enhancing the fertility of the soil. He explains his methods of cultivation, seeding and management. There are also chapters on year-round grazing, making silage for self-feeding, protein from forage crops, and pastures for pigs and poultry. He also details the roles individual herbs play in the prevention and treatment of disease. *Softcover, 224 pages. ISBN 978-1-601730-11-4*

Fertility Farming
by Newman Turner

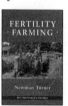

Fertility Farming explores an approach to farming that makes minimal use of plowing, eschews chemical fertilizers and pesticides, and emphasizes soil fertility via crop rotation, composting, cover cropping and manure application.

Turner holds that the foundation of the effectiveness of nature's husbandry is a fertile soil — and the measure of a fertile soil is its content of organic matter, ultimately, its *humus*. Upon a basis of humus, nature builds a complete structure of healthy life — without need for disease control of any kind. In fact, disease treatment is unnecessary in nature, as disease is the outcome of the unbalancing or perversion of the natural order — and serves as a warning that something is wrong. The avoidance of disease is therefore the simple practice of natural law. Much more than theory, this book was written to serve as a practical guide for farmers. Turner's advice for building a productive, profitable organic farming system rings as true today as it did sixty years ago when it was written. *Softcover, 272 pages. ISBN 978-1-601730-09-1*

Cure Your Own Cattle
by Newman Turner

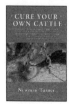

In this booklet, Newman Turner sought to "bring within the reach of the farmer a solution to his disease problems in a way in which drug and chemical treatments have never before achieved." He relied on his lifetime of observing animals and herbs in their natural environment to guide him in his experiments. The end result is his proclamation that freedom from animal diseases may be attained by the proper utilization of nature's provisions. While the subject of natural veterinary care has grown and matured, Turner's clear and simple systems and advice remind farmers of the true fundamentals that consistently work. *Softcover, 96 pages. ISBN 978-1-601730-08-4*

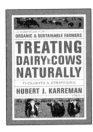